PEARSON CUSTOM LIBRARY

The Community College of Baltimo
Earth Science Laboratory

Laboratory manual for ERSC 999

PEARSON

Cover Art: Courtesy of Photodisc/Getty Images, Photoubrary.com, Robert Harding World Imagery, Getty Images/Photodisc.

The information, illustrations, and/or software contained in this book, and regarding the above mentioned programs, are provided "as is," without warranty of any kind, express or implied, including without limitation any warranty concerning the accuracy, adequacy, or completeness of such information. Neither the publisher, the authors, nor the copyright holders shall be responsible for any claims attributable to errors, omissions, or other inaccuracies contained in this book. Nor shall they be liable for direct, indirect, special, incidental, or consequential damages arising out of the use of such information or material.

The authors and publisher believe that the lab experiments described in this publication, when conducted in conformity with the safety precautions described herein and according to the school's laboratory safety procedures, are reasonably safe for the students for whom this manual is directed. Nonetheless, many of the described experiments are accompanied by some degree of risk, including human error, the failure or misuse of laboratory or electrical equipment, mismeasurement, spills of chemicals, and exposure to sharp objects, heat, body fluids, blood or other biologics. The authors and publisher disclaim any liability arising from such risks in connections with any of the experiments contained in this manual. If students have questions or problems with materials, procedures, or instructions on any experiment, they should always ask their instructor for help before proceeding.

Printed in the United States of America
24 16

Attention bookstores: For permission to return any unsold stock, contact us at *pe-uscustomreturns@pearson.com*.

Pearson Learning Solutions, 501 Boylston Street, Suite 900, Boston, MA 02116
A Pearson Education Company
www.pearsoned.com

ISBN 10: 0-558-19586-5
ISBN 13: 978-0-558-19586-1

Table of Contents

The Study of Minerals

The ability to identify minerals using the simplest of techniques is a necessity for the Earth scientist, especially those scientists working in the field. In this exercise you will become familiar with the common physical properties of minerals and learn how to use these properties to identify minerals (Figure 1). In order to understand the origin, classification, and alteration of rocks, which are for the most part aggregates (mixtures) of minerals, you must first be able to identify the minerals that comprise them.

Figure 1 Quartz crystals. Slender, six-sided, transparent crystals that will scratch glass. The shape of the crystals and their hardness are two physical properties used to identify this mineral. (Photo by E. J. Tarbuck)

Objectives

After you have completed this exercise, you should be able to:

1. Recognize and describe the physical properties of minerals.
2. Use a mineral identification key to name minerals.
3. Identify several minerals by sight.
4. List the uses of several minerals that are mined.

Materials

hand lens

Materials Supplied by Your Instructor

mineral samples	dilute hydrochloric acid
streak plate	set of quartz crystals
magnet	(various sizes)
glass plate	contact goniometer
binocular microscope	crystal growth solution(s)

Terms

mineral	translucent	cleavage plane
rock-forming mineral	transparent	direction of cleavage
	color	
luster	streak	fracture
metallic luster	hardness	specific gravity
nonmetallic luster	crystal form	magnetism
	contact goniometer	striations
opaque	cleavage	tenacity

Introduction

A **mineral** is a naturally occurring, inorganic solid with an orderly internal arrangement of atoms (called *crystalline structure*) and a definite, but not fixed, chemical composition. Some minerals, such as gold and diamond, are single chemical elements. However, most minerals are compounds consisting of two or more elements. For example, the mineral halite is composed

From *Applications and Investigations in Earth Science,* Sixth Edition, Edward J. Tarbuck, Frederick K. Lutgens, Kenneth G. Pinzke. Copyright © 2009 by Pearson Education, Inc. Published by Pearson Prentice Hall. All rights reserved.

Table 1   Mineral Uses

MINERAL	USE
Chalcopyrite	Mined for copper
Feldspar	Ceramics and porcelain
Fluorite	Used in steel manufacturing
Galena	Mined for lead
Graphite	Pencil "lead," lubricant
Gypsum	Drywall, plaster of paris, wallboard
Halite	Table salt, road salt, source of sodium and chlorine
Hematite	Mined for iron
Magnetite	Mined for iron
Pyrite	Mined for sulfur and iron
Quartz	In the pure form, for making glass
Sphalerite	Mined for zinc
Talc	Used in ceramics, paint, talcum powder

of the elements sodium and chlorine. The distinctive crystalline structure and chemical composition of a mineral give it a unique set of physical properties such as its luster, its hardness, and how it breaks. The fact that each mineral has its own characteristic physical and chemical properties can be used to distinguish one mineral from another.

Of the nearly 4,000 known minerals, only a few hundred have any current economic value. An example would be the mineral gypsum, used for making drywall and wallboard. Table 1 lists a few of the minerals that are mined as well as their uses. Of the remaining minerals, no more than a few dozen are abundant. Collectively, these few often occur with each other in the rocks of Earth's crust and are classified as the **rock-forming minerals**.

Physical Properties of Minerals

The physical properties of minerals are those properties that can be determined by observation or by performing some simple tests. The primary physical properties that are determined for all minerals include optical properties (in particular, luster, the ability to transmit light, color, and streak), hardness, crystal form, cleavage or fracture, and specific gravity. Secondary (or "special") properties, including magnetism, taste, feel, striations, tenacity, and the reaction with dilute hydrochloric acid, are also useful in identifying certain minerals.

Optical Properties

Of the many optical properties of minerals, four—luster, the ability to transmit light, color, and streak—are frequently determined for hand specimens.

Luster   Luster describes the manner in which light is reflected from the surface of a mineral. Any mineral that shines with a metal-like appearance has a **metallic luster**. Those minerals that do not have a metallic lus-

ter are termed **nonmetallic** and may have one of a variety of lusters that include vitreous (glassy), pearly (like a pearl), or earthy (dull, like soil or concrete). In general, many minerals with metallic luster produce a dark gray, black, or other distinctively colored powder when they are rubbed on a hard porcelain plate (this property, called *streak*, will be investigated later).

Observe the mineral photographs shown in Figures 2 through 13. The minerals illustrated in Figures 5 and 6 have definite metallic lusters. The minerals in Figure 9 have nonmetallic, vitreous (glassy) lusters. Some minerals, such as hematite (Figure 7), occur in both metallic and nonmetallic varieties.

Transmission of Light   The ability of a mineral to transmit light can be described as either **opaque**, when no light is transmitted (e.g., Figure 3); **translucent**, when light but not an image is transmitted; or, **transparent**, when an image is visible through the mineral (e.g., Figure 1). In general, most minerals with a metallic luster are opaque, while vitreous minerals are either translucent or transparent.

Examine the mineral specimens provided by your instructor, and answer the following questions.

1. How many of your specimens can be grouped into each of the following luster types?

   Metallic: _____   Nonmetallic-glassy: _____

2. How many of your specimens are transparent, and how many are opaque?

   Transparent: _____   Opaque: _____

Color   Color, although an obvious feature of minerals, may also be misleading. For example, slight impurities in a mineral may result in one sample of the mineral having one color while a different sample of the same mineral may have an entirely different color. *Thus, color is one of the least reliable physical properties.*

3. Observe the minerals in Figure 8. Both of the minerals shown are varieties of the same mineral, quartz. What is the reason for the variety of colors that quartz exhibits?

   _____

   _____

4. Examine the mineral specimens supplied by your instructor, and describe those that appear to be the same mineral but with variable colors.

   _____

   _____

Streak   The streak of a mineral is the color of the fine powder of a mineral obtained by rubbing a corner across a piece of unglazed porcelain—called a *streak plate*. Whereas the color of a mineral may vary from sample to sample, its streak usually does not and is therefore the more reliable property (see Figure 7). In

Figure 2 Fluorite (left), halite (center), and calcite (right) exhibit smooth cleavage planes that are produced when the mineral is broken. (Photo by GeoScience Resources/American Geological Institute).

Figure 5 Galena. An ore of lead with a high specific gravity.

Figure 3 Sphalerite. An ore of zinc.

Figure 6 Pyrite. A brassy-yellow mineral with a metallic luster that is commonly known as "fool's gold."

Figure 4 Graphite. A soft silver-gray mineral.

Figure 7 Hematite. An ore of iron that has both a metallic (right) and nonmetallic (left) form.

Figure 8 Two varieties of the mineral quartz. Rose quartz (right) and smoky quartz (left).

Figure 11 Augite. A dark green to black, rock-forming, pyroxene mineral.

Figure 9 Biotite mica (black) and muscovite mica (light color) are similar in appearance, except for color.

Figure 12 Potassium feldspar, variety microcline.

Figure 10 Hornblende. A generally green to black, rock-forming, amphibole mineral.

Figure 13 Plagioclase feldspar, variety labradorite.

many cases, the color of a mineral's streak may not be the same as the color of the mineral. [*Note:* Minerals that have about the same hardness as, or are harder than, a streak plate (about 7 on Mohs scale of hardness), may not powder or produce a streak.]

5. Select three of the mineral specimens provided by your instructor. Do they exhibit a streak? If so, is the streak the same color as the mineral specimen?

	COLOR OF SPECIMEN	STREAK
Specimen 1:	_____	_____
Specimen 2:	_____	_____
Specimen 3:	_____	_____

Hardness

Hardness, one of the most useful diagnostic properties of a mineral, is a measure of the resistance of a mineral to abrasion or scratching. It is a relative property in that a harder substance will scratch, or cut into, a softer one.

In order to establish a common system for determining hardness, Friedrich Mohs (1773–1839), a German mineralogist, developed a reference scale of mineral hardness. The Mohs scale of hardness (Figure 14), widely used today by geologists and engineers, uses 10 index minerals as a reference set to determine the hardness of other minerals. The hardness value of 1 is assigned to the softest mineral in the set, talc, and 10 is assigned to the hardest mineral, diamond. Higher-numbered minerals will scratch lower-numbered minerals. For example, quartz, with a hardness of 7, will scratch calcite, which has a hardness of 3. It should be remembered that Mohs scale is a *relative ranking* and does *not* imply that mineral number 2, gypsum, is twice as hard as mineral 1, talc.

Most people do not have a set of Mohs reference minerals available. However, by knowing the hardness of some common objects, such as those listed on Mohs scale in Figure 14, a hardness value can be assigned to a mineral. For example, a mineral that has a hardness greater than 5.5 will scratch glass. Table 2 can serve as a guide for determining the hardness of a mineral.

6. Test the hardness of several of the mineral specimens provided by your instructor by rubbing any two together to determine which are hard (the minerals that do the scratching) and which are soft (the minerals that are scratched). Doing this will give you an indication of what

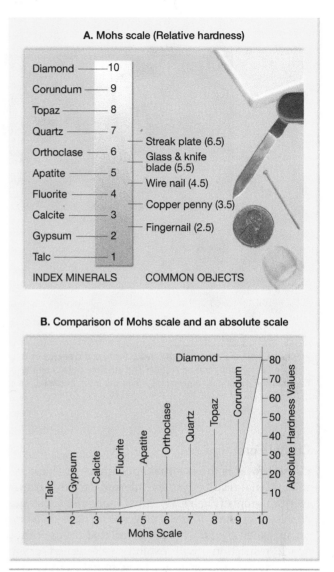

Figure 14 Hardness scales. **A.** Mohs scale of hardness, with the hardness of some common objects. **B.** Relationship between Mohs relative hardness scale and an absolute hardness scale.

is meant by the term "relative hardness" of minerals.

7. Use the hardness guide in Table 2 to find an example of a mineral supplied by your instructor that falls in each of the three categories.

Table 2   **Hardness guide**

HARDNESS	DESCRIPTION
Less than 2.5	A mineral that can be scratched by your fingernail (hardness = 2.5).
2.5 to 5.5	A mineral that cannot be scratched by your fingernail (hardness = 2.5), and cannot scratch glass (hardness = 5.5).
Greater than 5.5	A mineral that scratches glass (hardness = 5.5).

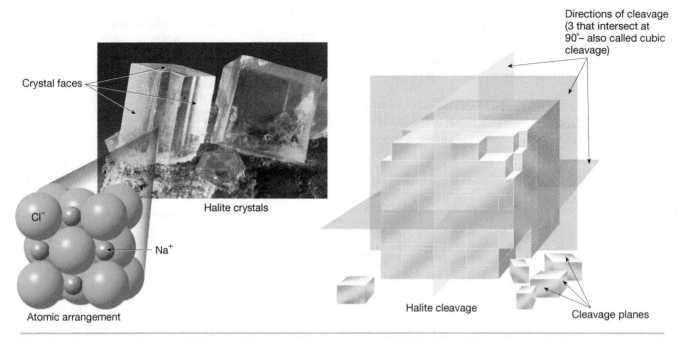

Crystal faces

Halite crystals

Cl⁻

Na⁺

Atomic arrangement

Directions of cleavage
(3 that intersect at
90°– also called cubic
cleavage)

Halite cleavage

Cleavage planes

Figure 15 Atomic arrangement, crystal form, and cleavage of the mineral halite. Halite (NaCl) contains sodium and chlorine atoms arranged in a one-to-one ratio forming a cube. The internal, orderly arrangement of atoms produces the external cubic crystal form of the mineral. Planes of weak bonding between atoms in the internal crystalline structure are responsible for halite's cubic cleavage.

Crystal Form

Crystal form is the external appearance or shape of a mineral that results from the internal, orderly arrangement of atoms (Figure 15). Most inorganic substances consist of crystals. The flat external surfaces on a crystal are called *crystal faces*. A mineral that forms without space restrictions will exhibit well-formed crystal faces. However, most of the time, minerals must compete for space, and the result is a dense intergrown mass in which crystals do not exhibit their crystal form, especially to the unaided eye.

8. At the discretion of your instructor, you may be asked to grow crystals by evaporating prepared concentrated solutions. Following the specific directions of your instructor, and after you have completed your experiment(s), write a brief paragraph summarizing your observations.

_____

_____

_____

One of the most useful instruments for measuring the angle between crystal faces on large crystals is the **contact goniometer** (Figure 16).

9. The mineral shown in Figure 1 has a well-developed crystal form with six faces that intersect at

about 120° and come to a point. Two varieties of the same mineral are shown in Figure 8. Why do those in Figure 8 not exhibit crystal form?

_____

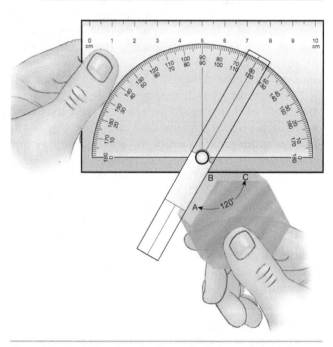

Figure 16 Contact goniometer. To use the instrument, hold the straight edge of the protractor in contact with one crystal face and the edge of the celluloid strip in contact with the other face. The angle is read where the fine line on the celluloid strip overlaps the degrees on the protractor. For example, the angle between the adjacent crystal faces on the mineral illustrated (angle ABC) is 120°.

10. Select one of the photographed minerals, other than Figure 1, that exhibits its crystal form and describe its shape.

    Figure _____ : _____

11. Observe the various size crystals of the mineral quartz on display in the lab. Use the contact goniometer to measure the angle between similar, adjacent crystal faces on several crystals. Then write a statement relating the angle between adjacent crystal faces to the size of the crystal.

    _____

    _____

Cleavage and Fracture

Cleavage is the tendency of some minerals to break along regular planes of weak bonding between atoms in the internal crystalline structure (see Figure 15). When broken, minerals that exhibit cleavage produce smooth, flat surfaces, called **cleavage planes**.

Cleavage is described by (1) noting the number of **directions of cleavage**, which is the number of different sets of planes that form the surfaces of a mineral crystal when it cleaves, and (2) the angle(s) at which the directions of cleavage meet (see Figure 15). Each cleavage plane of a mineral crystal that has a different orientation is counted as a different direction of cleavage. When two or more cleavage planes are parallel or line up with each other, they are counted only once, as one direction of cleavage. Minerals may have one, two, three, four, or more directions of cleavage (Figure 17).

Number of Cleavage Directions	Shape	Sketch	Directions of Cleavage	Sample
1	Flat sheets			 Muscovite
2 at 90°	Elongated form with rectangle cross section (prism)		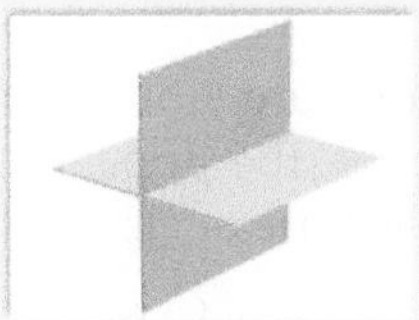	 Feldspar
2 not at 90°	Elongated form with parallelogram cross section (prism)			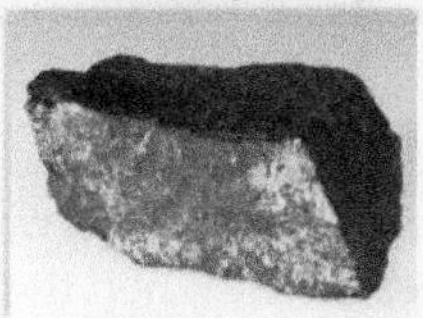 Hornblende
3 at 90°	Cube	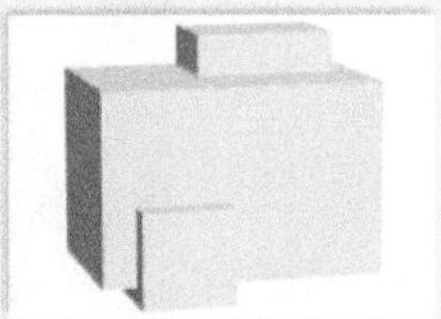	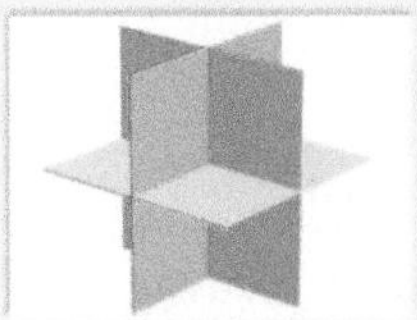	 Halite
3 not at 90°	Rhombohedron	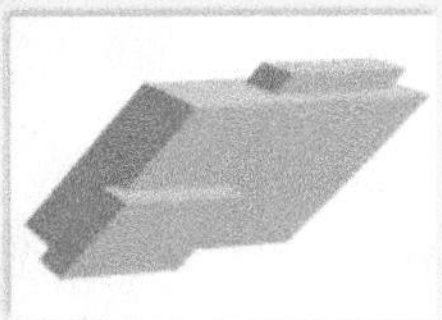		 Calcite
4	Octahedron		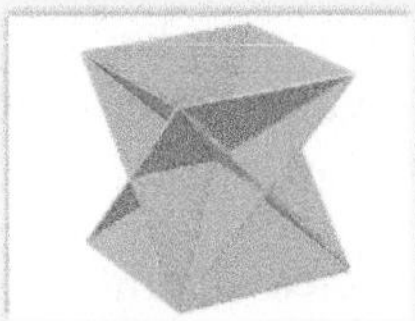	 Fluorite

Figure 17   Common cleavage directions of minerals.

7

Observe the minerals shown in Figures 5 and 15. These minerals have broken with regularity and exhibit cleavage. The specimens shown are in the form of a cube. Although there are six planes of cleavage surrounding each specimen, each exhibits only three directions of cleavage: top and bottom form one parallel set of planes—hence the first direction of cleavage; the two sides are a second parallel set—a second direction of cleavage; and the front and back form the third direction of cleavage. The cleavage of both minerals is described as three directions of cleavage that intersect at 90° (also commonly called *cubic cleavage*) (see Figure 17).

Cleavage and crystal form are *not* the same. Some mineral crystals cleave while others do not. Cleavage is determined by the bonds that hold atoms together, while crystal form results from the internal, orderly arrangement of the atoms. The best way to determine whether or not a mineral cleaves is to break it and carefully examine the results.

Minerals that do not exhibit cleavage when broken are said to **fracture** (see Figure 4). Fracturing can be irregular, splintery, or conchoidal (smooth curved surfaces resembling broken glass). Some minerals may cleave in one or two directions and also exhibit fracturing (see Figure 12).

12. The minerals shown in Figure 9 have one direction of cleavage. Describe the appearance of a mineral that exhibits this type of cleavage.

_____

13. Observe the photograph of calcite, the mineral on the right in Figure 2. Several smooth, flat planes result when the mineral is broken.

   a. How many planes of cleavage are present on the specimen?

   _____ planes of cleavage

   b. How many directions of cleavage are present on the specimen?

   _____ directions of cleavage

   c. The cleavage directions meet at (90° angles, angles other than 90°). Circle your answer.

14. Select one mineral specimen supplied by your instructor that exhibits cleavage. Describe its cleavage by completing the following statement.

   _____ directions of cleavage at _____ degrees

Specific Gravity

Specific gravity is a number that represents the ratio of the weight of a mineral to the weight of an equal volume of water. For example, the mineral quartz, Figures 1 and 8, has a specific gravity of 2.65; this means it weighs 2.65 times more than an equal volume of water. The mineral galena, Figure 5, with a specific gravity of 7.4, feels heavy when held in your hand. With a little practice, you can estimate the specific gravity of a mineral by hefting it in your hand. The average specific gravity of minerals is about 2.7, but some metallic minerals have a specific gravity two or three times greater than the average.

15. Find a mineral specimen supplied by your instructor that exhibits a high specific gravity by giving each mineral a heft in your hand.

Other Properties of Minerals

Luster, the ability to transmit light, hardness, color, streak, crystal form, cleavage or fracture, and specific gravity are the most basic and common physical properties used to identify minerals. However, other special properties can also be used to identify certain minerals. These other properties include:

Magnetism Magnetism is characteristic of minerals, such as magnetite, that have a high iron content and are attracted by a magnet. A variety of magnetite called *lodestone* is itself actually magnetic and will pick up paper clips (Figure 18).

Figure 18 Magnetite, variety lodestone, has polarity like a magnet and will attract iron objects.

Specimen Number	Luster	Hardness	Color	Streak	Fracture or / Cleavage (number of directions and angle of intersection)	Other Properties	Name	Economic Use or Rock-forming
1	Metalic	1	DG					
2	Nm	7	Amy					
4	Nm	7	Any					
9	M	2.5	SG					
11	Nm	6	Pink					
16	Nm	7	clear					
17	Nm	2	C					
18	NM	2	B					
19	Nm	3	C					
20	NM	2.5	C					
23	Nm	7	rose					
25	Nm	1	RB					

Figure 19 Mineral identification chart.

Specimen Number	Luster	Hardness	Color	Streak	Cleavage Fracture or (number of directions and angle of intersection)	Other Properties	Name	Economic Use or Rock-forming

Figure 19 Mineral identification chart (*continued*)

Taste The mineral halite (Figure 2, center) has a "salty" taste.

> CAUTION: Do not taste any minerals or other materials without knowing it is *absolutely* safe to do so.

Feel The mineral talc often feels "soapy," while the mineral graphite (Figure 4) has a "greasy" feel.

Striations Striations are closely spaced, fine lines on the crystal faces of some minerals. They resemble the surface of a phonograph record but are straight. Certain plagioclase feldspar minerals often exhibit striations on one cleavage surface (see Figure 13).

Tenacity Tenacity is the manner in which a substance resists breaking. Terms like *flexible* (a thin piece of plastic) and *brittle* (glass) are used to describe this property.

Reaction to Dilute Hydrochloric Acid A very small drop of dilute hydrochloric acid, when placed on a freshly exposed surface of some minerals, will cause them to "fizz" (effervesce) as the gas carbon dioxide is released. The test is often used to identify a group of minerals called the *carbonate minerals*. The mineral calcite, Figure 2 (right), (chemical name: calcium carbonate) is the most common carbonate mineral and is frequently found in rocks.

> CAUTION: Hydrochloric acid can discolor, decompose, and disintegrate mineral and rock samples. Use the acid only after you have received specific instructions on its use from your instructor. Never taste minerals that have had acid placed on them.

16. Following the directions given by your instructor, examine the mineral specimens to determine if any exhibit one or more of the special properties listed above.

Identification of Minerals

Having investigated the physical properties of minerals, you are now prepared to proceed with the identification of the minerals supplied by your instructor.

To identify a mineral, you must first determine, using available tools, as many of its physical properties as you can. Next, knowing the properties of the mineral, you proceed to a mineral identification key, which often functions like an outline, to narrow down the choices and arrive at a specific name. *As you complete the exercise, remember that the goal is to learn the procedure for identifying minerals through observation and not simply to put a name on them.*

Arrange your mineral specimens by placing them on a numbered sheet of paper. Locate the mineral identification chart, Figure 19, and write the numbers of your mineral specimens, in order, under the column labeled "Specimen Number."

Using a Mineral Identification Key

Figure 20 is a mineral identification key that uses the property of luster as the primary division of minerals into two groups, those with metallic lusters and those with nonmetallic lusters. Color (either dark- or light-colored) is used as a secondary division for the nonmetallic minerals. Examine the mineral identification key closely to see how it is arranged.

17. Use the mineral identification key (Figure 20). What would be the name of the mineral with these properties: nonmetallic luster, light-colored, softer than a fingernail, produces small, thin plates or sheets when scratched by a fingernail, white color, and a "soapy" feel?

    Mineral name:

    (Check your answer with your instructor before proceeding.)

18. Complete the mineral identification chart, Figure 19, by listing the properties of each of the mineral specimens supplied by your instructor. Use the mineral identification key, Figure 20, to determine the name of each of the minerals.

19. Use Table 1, *Mineral Uses*, to determine which of the minerals you identify have an economic use.

    List their use in the column to the right of their name on the mineral identification chart, Figure 19.

20. The mineral photographs, Figure 2 (right, calcite) and Figures 8 through 13, show some of the most common rock-forming minerals. If your mineral specimens include examples of these minerals, indicate that they are rock-forming in the column to the right of their name on your mineral identification chart.

Minerals on the Internet

Apply the concepts from this exercise to an investigation of the mineral resources in your home state by completing the corresponding online activity on the *Applications & Investigations in Earth Science* website at http://prenhall.com/earthsciencelab

METALLIC MINERALS

Hardness	Streak	Other Diagnostic Properties	Name (Chemical Composition)
Harder than glass	Black	Black; magnetic; hardness = 6; specific gravity = 5.2; often granular	Magnetite (Fe_3O_4)
	Greenish-black	Brass yellow; hardness = 6; specific gravity = 5.2; generally an aggregate of cubic crystals	Pyrite (FeS_2)-fool's gold
	Red-brown	Gray or reddish brown; hardness = 5–6; specific gravity = 5; platy appearance	Hematite (Fe_2O_3)
Softer than glass but harder than a finger nail	Greenish-black	Golden yellow; hardness = 4; specific gravity = 4.2; massive	Chalcopyrite ($CuFeS_2$)
	Gray-black	Silvery gray; hardness = 2.5; specific gravity = 7.6 (very heavy); good cubic cleavage	Galena (PbS)
	Yellow-brown	Yellow brown to dark brown; hardness variable (1–6); specific gravity = 3.5–4; often found in rounded masses; earthy appearance	Limonite ($Fe_2O_3 \cdot H_2O$)
	Gray-black	Black to bronze; tarnishes to purples and greens; hardness = 3; specific gravity = 5; massive	Bornite (Cu_5FeS_4)
Softer than your fingernail	Dark gray	Silvery gray; hardness = 1 (very soft); specific gravity = 2.2; massive to platy; writes on paper (pencil lead); feels greasy	Graphite (C)

NONMETALLIC MINERALS

Hardness	Cleavage	Other Diagnostic Properties	Name (Chemical Composition)
Dark colored / Harder than glass	Cleavage Present	Greenish black to black; hardness = 5–6; specific gravity = 3.4; fair cleavage, two directions at nearly 90 degrees	Augite (Ca, Mg, Fe, Al silicate)
		Black to greenish black; hardness = 5–6; specific gravity = 3.2; fair cleavage, two directions at nearly 60 degrees and 120 degrees	Hornblende (Ca, Na, Mg, Fe, OH, Al silicate)
		Red to reddish brown; hardness = 6.5–7.5; conchoidal fracture; glassy luster	Garnet (Fe, Mg, Ca, Al silicate)
	Cleavage not prominent	Gray to brown; hardness = 9; specific gravity = 4; hexagonal crystals common	Corundum (Al_2O_3)
		Dark brown to black; hardness = 7; conchoidal fracture; glassy luster	Smoky quartz (SiO_2)
		Olive green; hardness = 6.5–7; small glassy grains	Olivine $(Mg, Fe)_2SiO_4$

Figure 20 Mineral identification key.

NONMETALLIC MINERALS

	Hardness	Cleavage	Other Diagnostic Properties	Name (Chemical Composition)
Dark colored (continued)	Softer than glass but harder than a fingernail	Cleavage present	Yellow brown to black; hardness = 4; good cleavage in six directions, light yellow streak that has the smell of sulfur	Sphalerite (ZnS)
			Dark brown to black; hardness = 2.5–3, excellent cleavage in one direction; elastic in thin sheets; black mica	Biotite mica (K, Mg, Fe, OH, Al silicate)
		Cleavage absent	Generally tarnished to brown or green; hardness = 2.5; specific gravity = 9; massive	Native copper (Cu)
	Softer than your fingernail	Cleavage not prominent	Reddish brown; hardness = 1–5; specific gravity = 4–5; red streak; earthy appearance	Hematite (Fe_2O_3)
			Yellow brown; hardness = 1–3; specific gravity = 3.5; earthy appearance; powders easily	Limonite ($Fe_2O_3 \cdot H_2O$)
Light Colored	Harder than glass	Cleavage present	Pink or white to gray; hardness = 6; specific gravity = 2.6; two directions of cleavage at nearly right angles	Potassium feldspar ($KAlSi_3O_8$) (pink)
				Plagioclase feldspar ($NaAlSi_3O_8$ to $CaAl_2Si_2O_8$) (white to gray)
		Cleavage absent	Any color; hardness = 7; specific gravity = 2.65; conchoidal fracture; glassy appearance; varieties: milky (white), rose (pink), smoky (gray), amethyst (violet)	Quartz (SiO_2)
	Softer than glass but harder than a finger nail	Cleavage present	White, yellowish to colorless; hardness = 3; three directions of cleavage at 75 degrees (rhombo-hedral); effervesces in HCl; often transparent	Calcite ($CaCO_3$)
			White to colorless; hardness = 2.5; three directions of cleavage at 90 degrees (cubic); salty taste	Halite (NaCl)
			Yellow, purple, green, colorless; hardness = 4; white streak; translucent to transparent; four directions of cleavage	Fluorite (CaF_2)
	Softer than your fingernail	Cleavage present	Colorless; hardness = 2–2.5; transparent and elastic in thin sheets; excellent cleavage in one direction; light mica	Muscovite mica (K, OH, Al silicate)
			White to transparent, hardness = 2; when in sheets; is flexible but not elastic; varieties: selenite (transparent, three directions of cleavage); satin spar (fibrous, silky luster); alabaster (aggregate of small crystals)	Gypsum ($CaSO_4 \cdot 2H_2O$)
		Cleavage not prominent	White, pink, green; hardness = 1–2; forms in thin plates; soapy feel; pearly luster	Talc (Mg silicate)
			Yellow; hardness = 1–2.5	Sulfur (S)
			White; hardness = 2; smooth feel; earthy odor; when moistened, has typical clay texture	Kaolinite (Hydrous Al silicate)
			Pale to dark reddish brown; hardness = 1–3; dull luster; earthy; often contains spheroidal-shaped particles; not a true mineral	Bauxite (Hydrous Al oxide)

Figure 20   Mineral identification key (*continued*)

Notes and calculations.

The Study of Minerals

Date Due: _____

Name: _____

Date: _____

Class: _____

After you have finished this exercise, complete the following questions. You may have to refer to the exercise for assistance or to locate specific answers. Be prepared to submit this summary/report to your instructor at the designated time.

1. Describe the procedure for identifying a mineral and arriving at its name.

   _____

   _____

   _____

2. Name the physical property of a mineral that is described by each of the following statements.

   PHYSICAL PROPERTY

   Breaks along smooth planes: _____

   Scratches glass: _____

   Shines like a metal: _____

   A red-colored powder on unglazed porcelain:

   _____

3. Describe the shape of a mineral that has three directions of cleavage that intersect at 90°.

   _____

4. Name two minerals you identified that have good cleavage. Describe the cleavage of each mineral.

   MINERAL   **CLEAVAGE**

   _____ : _____

   _____ : _____

5. Select five minerals you identified, and list their names and physical properties.

   _____ : _____

   _____

   _____

   _____ : _____

   _____

   _____

   _____ : _____

   _____

   _____

   _____ : _____

   _____

   _____

   _____ : _____

   _____

   _____

6. Name one mineral that you identified that has an economic use.

   MINERAL   **MINED FOR**

   _____ : _____

7. List the name and hardness of two minerals you identified.

   MINERAL   HARDNESS

   _____ : _____

   _____ : _____

A.   B.

Figure 21   Two mineral specimens for use with question 13.

8. How many directions of cleavage do the feldspar minerals—potassium feldspar and plagioclase feldspar—have?

   ___ directions of cleavage

9. What was your conclusion concerning the angles between similar crystal faces on different size crystals of the same mineral?

   _____

13. Referring to the minerals illustrated in Figure 21, list the physical properties of each mineral that can be determined from its photograph.

    A: _____

    _____

    _____

    _____

10. List the name(s) of the minerals you identified that had a special property such as magnetism or feel. Write the special property that you observed next to the name of the mineral.

    MINERAL   SPECIAL PROPERTY

    _____ : _____
    _____ : _____
    _____ : _____

    B: _____

    _____

    _____

    _____

11. What physical property most distinguishes biotite mica from muscovite mica?

    _____

12. Selecting from the minerals illustrated in Figures 1 through 13, list, by name, one mineral that exhibits each of the following:

    one direction of cleavage: _____

    striations: _____

    multiple colors: _____

    cubic cleavage: _____

    nonmetallic, vitreous luster: _____

    fracture: _____

    metallic luster: _____

14. The mineral identification key, Figure 20, uses the property of luster as its primary division of minerals. Develop and describe an alternative classification key that uses another property, or properties, to divide minerals into groups.

    _____

    _____

    _____

    _____

    _____

    _____

    _____

    _____

16

Common Rocks

To an Earth scientist, rocks represent much more than usable substances. They are the materials of the Earth; understanding their origin and how they change allows us to begin to understand Earth and its processes. It is often said that "the history of Earth is written in the rocks"—we just have to be smart enough to read the "words."

In this exercise, you will investigate some of the common rocks that are found on and near Earth's surface. The criteria used to classify a rock as being of either igneous, sedimentary, or metamorphic origin are examined, as well as the procedure for identifying rocks within each of these three families.

Objectives

After you have completed this exercise, you should be able to:

1. Examine a rock and determine if it is an igneous, sedimentary, or metamorphic rock.
2. List and define the terms used to describe the textures of igneous, sedimentary, and metamorphic rocks.
3. Name the dominant mineral(s) found in the most common igneous, sedimentary, and metamorphic rocks.
4. Use a classification key to identify a rock.
5. Recognize and name some of the common rocks by sight.

Materials

metric ruler   hand lens

Materials Supplied by Your Instructor

igneous rocks   dilute hydrochloric acid
sedimentary rocks   streak plate

metamorphic rocks   glass plate
hand lens or binocular   copper penny
  microscope

Terms

rock	weathering	composition
rock cycle	sediment	detrital material
igneous rock	lithification	chemical material
magma	metamorphic	foliation
sedimentary	rock	texture
rock		

Introduction

Most **rocks** are aggregates (mixtures) of minerals. However, there are some rocks that are composed essentially of one mineral found in large impure quantities. The rock limestone, consisting almost entirely of the mineral calcite, is a good example.

Rocks are classified into three types, based on the processes that formed them. One of the most useful devices for understanding rock types and the geologic processes that transform one rock type into another is the **rock cycle**. The cycle, shown in Figure 1, illustrates the various Earth materials and uses arrows to indicate chemical and physical processes. As you examine the rock cycle and read the following definitions, notice the references to the origin of each rock type.

The three types of rock are igneous, sedimentary, and metamorphic.

Igneous Igneous rocks (Figures 2–9) are the solidified products of once molten material called **magma**. The distinguishing feature of most igneous rocks is an interlocking arrangement of mineral crystals that forms as the molten material cools and crystals grow. *Intrusive* igneous rocks form below the surface of Earth, while those that form at the surface from lava are termed *extrusive*.

Sedimentary These rocks (Figures 10–17) form at or near Earth's surface from the accumulated products of

From *Applications and Investigations in Earth Science,* Sixth Edition, Edward J. Tarbuck, Frederick K. Lutgens, Kenneth G. Pinzke. Copyright

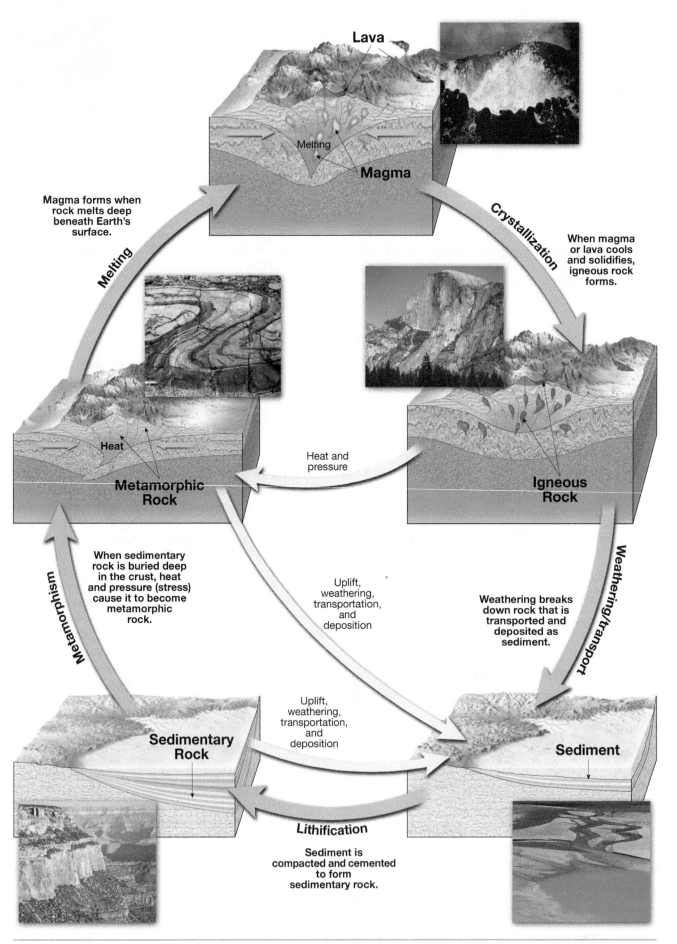

Lava

Melting

Magma

Magma forms when rock melts deep beneath Earth's surface.

Melting

Crystallization

When magma or lava cools and solidifies, igneous rock forms.

Heat and pressure

Metamorphic Rock

Heat

Igneous Rock

Metamorphism

When sedimentary rock is buried deep in the crust, heat and pressure (stress) cause it to become metamorphic rock.

Uplift, weathering, transportation, and deposition

Weathering/transport

Weathering breaks down rock that is transported and deposited as sediment.

Sedimentary Rock

Uplift, weathering, transportation, and deposition

Sediment

Lithification

Sediment is compacted and cemented to form sedimentary rock.

Figure 1 The rock cycle illustrating the role of the various geologic processes that act to transform one rock type into another.

weathering, called **sediment**. These products may be solid particles or material that was formerly dissolved and then precipitated by either inorganic or organic processes. The process of **lithification** transforms the sediment into hard rock. Since sedimentary rocks form at, or very near. Earth's surface, they often contain organic matter, or fossils, or both. The layering (or bedding) that develops as sediment is sorted by, and settled out from, a transporting material (usually water or air) helps make sedimentary rocks recognizable.

Metamorphic These rocks (Figures 18–25) form below Earth's surface where high temperatures, pressures, and/or chemical fluids change preexisting rocks without melting them.

Minerals are identified by using their physical and chemical properties. However, rock types and the names of individual rocks are determined by describing their *textures* and *compositions*. The key to success in rock identification lies in learning to accurately determine and describe these properties.

Texture refers to the shape, arrangement, and size of mineral grains in a rock. The shape and arrangement of mineral grains help determine the type (igneous, sedimentary, or metamorphic) of rock. Mineral grain size is often used to separate rocks within a particular type. Each rock type uses different terms to describe its textures.

Composition refers to the minerals that are found in a rock. Often the larger mineral grains can be identified by sight or by using their physical properties. In some cases, small mineral grains may require the use of a hand lens or microscope. Occasionally, very small grains cannot be identified with the normal magnification of a microscope. Practice and increased familiarity with the minerals will make this assessment easier.

Comparing Igneous, Sedimentary, and Metamorphic Rocks

One of the first steps in the identification of rocks is to determine the rock type. Each of the three rock types has a somewhat unique appearance that helps to distinguish one type from the other.

Examine the specimens of the three rock types supplied by your instructor, as well as the photographs of the rocks in Figures 2–25. Then answer the following questions.

1. Which two of the three rock types appear to be made primarily of intergrown crystals?

_____ rocks and _____ rocks

2. Which one of the two rock types you listed in question 1 has the mineral crystals aligned or arranged so that they are oriented in the same direction in a linear, linelike manner?

3. Which one of the two rock types you listed in question 1 has the mineral crystals in most of the rocks arranged in a dense interlocking mass with no alignment?

4. Of the three rock types, (igneous, sedimentary, metamorphic) rocks often contain haphazardly arranged pieces or fragments, rather than crystals. Circle your answer.

Igneous Rock Identification

Igneous rocks form from the cooling and crystallization of magma. The interlocking network of mineral crystals that develop as the molten material cools gives most igneous rocks their distinctive crystalline appearance.

Textures of Igneous Rocks

The rate of cooling of the magma determines the size of the interlocking crystals found in igneous rocks. The slower the cooling rate, the larger the mineral crystals. The five principal textures of igneous rocks are:

Coarse Grained (or *phaneritic*) The majority of mineral crystals are of a uniform size and large enough to be identifiable without a microscope. This texture occurs when magma cools slowly inside Earth.

Fine Grained (or *aphanitic*) Very small crystals, which are generally not identifiable without strong magnification, develop when molten material cools quickly on, or very near, the surface of Earth.

Porphyritic Two very contrasting sizes of crystals are caused by magma having two different rates of cooling. The larger crystals are termed *phenocrysts*; and the smaller, surrounding crystals are termed *groundmass* (or *matrix*).

Glassy No mineral crystals develop because of very rapid cooling. This lack of crystals causes the rock to have a glassy appearance. In some cases, rapidly escaping gases may produce a frothy appearance similar to spun glass.

Fragmental The rock contains broken, angular fragments of rocky materials produced during an explosive volcanic eruption.

Examine the igneous rock photographs in Figures 2–9. Then answer the following questions.

5. The igneous rock illustrated in Figure 2 is made of large mineral crystals that are all about the same size. The rock formed from magma that cooled (slowly, rapidly) (inside, on the surface of) Earth. Circle your answers.

Igneous Rocks

Figure 2   Granite, a common coarse-grained, intrusive igneous rock.

Figure 3   Rhyolite, a fine-grained, extrusive rock.

Figure 4   Diorite, a coarse-grained igneous rock.

Figure 5   Andesite porphry, an igneous rock with a porphyritic texture.

Figure 6   Basalt, a fine-grained igneous rock.

Figure 7   Gabbro, a coarse-grained, intrusive igneous rock.

Figure 8   Obsidian, an igneous rock with a glassy texture.

Figure 9   Pumice, a glassy rock containing numerous tiny voids.

Sedimentary Rocks

Figure 10   Conglomerate, a detrital sedimentary rock.

Figure 11   Sandstone, a common detrital sedimentary rock.

Figure 12   Shale, a detrital sedimentary rock composed of very fine grains.

Figure 13   Breccia, a detrital sedimentary rock containing large, angular fragments.

Figure 14   Fossiliferous limestone, a biochemical sedimentary rock.

Figure 15   Coquina, a biochemical limestone consisting of visible shells and shell fragments, loosely cemented.

Figure 16   Rock salt, a chemical sedimentary rock formed as water evaporates.

Figure 17   Bituminous coal, a sedimentary rock composed of altered plant remains.

Metamorphic Rocks

Figure 18 Slate, a fine-grained, foliated metamorphic rock.

Figure 19 Phyllite, a foliated metamorphic rock with barely visible grains.

Figure 20 Schist, a foliated metamorphic rock with visible grains (variety: garnet-mica schist).

Figure 21 Gneiss, a foliated-banded metamorphic rock that often forms during intensive metamorphism.

Figure 22 Schist, variety mica schist.

Figure 23 Marble, a nonfoliated metamorphic rock that forms from the metamorphism of the sedimentary rock limestone.

Figure 24 Quartzite, a nonfoliated metamorphic rock composed of fused quartz grains.

Figure 25 Anthracite coal, often called hard coal, forms from the metamorphism of bituminous coal.

6. The rock shown in Figure 6 is made of mineral crystals that are all small and not identifiable without a microscope. The rock formed from magma that cooled (slowly, rapidly) (inside, on/near the surface of) Earth. Circle your answers.

7. The igneous rock in Figure 5 has a porphyritic texture. The large crystals are called _____, and the surrounding, smaller crystals are called _____.

8. The rocks in Figures 2 and 3 have nearly the same mineral composition. What fact about the mineral crystals in the rocks makes their appearances so different? What caused this difference?

_____

_____

Select a coarse-grained rock from the igneous rock specimens supplied by your instructor and examine the mineral crystals closely using a hand lens or microscope.

9. Sketch a diagram showing the arrangement of the mineral crystals in the igneous rock specimen you examined in the space provided below. Indicate the scale of your sketch by writing the appropriate length within the ( ) provided on the bar scale.

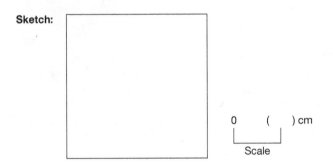

Sketch:

0   (   ) cm

Scale

Composition of Igneous Rocks

The specific mineral composition of an igneous rock is ultimately determined by the chemical composition of the magma from which it crystallized. However, the minerals found in igneous rocks can be arranged into four groups. Each group can be identified by observing the proportion of dark-colored minerals compared to light-colored minerals. The four groups are

Felsic (or *granitic*) Composed mainly of the light-colored minerals quartz and potassium feldspars. Dark-colored minerals account for less than 15% of the minerals in rocks found in this group.

Intermediate (or *andesitic*) A mixture of both light-colored and dark-colored minerals. Dark minerals comprise about 15% to 45% of these rocks.

Mafic (or *basaltic*) Dark-colored minerals such as pyroxene and olivine account for over 45% of the composition of these rocks.

Ultramafic Composed almost entirely of the dark-colored minerals pyroxene and olivine, these rocks are rarely observed on Earth's surface. However, the ultramafic rock peridotite is believed to be a major constituent of Earth's upper mantle.

10. Estimate the percentage of dark minerals contained in the igneous rock in Figure 4. (You may find the color index at the top of Figure 26, *Igneous & Rock Identification Key,* helpful.) The rock's color is (light, medium, dark, very dark). Circle your answer.

11. The rocks shown in Figures 3 and 6 have the same texture. What fact about the mineral crystals makes their appearances so different?

_____

Using an Igneous Rock Identification Key

The name of an igneous rock can be found by first determining its texture and color (an indication of mineral composition), identifying visible mineral grains, and then using an igneous rock identification key such as the one shown in Figure 26 to determine the name.

For example, the igneous rock shown in Figure 2 has a coarse-grained texture and is light-colored (quartz and potassium feldspar dominant). Intersecting the light-colored column with the coarse-grained row on the igneous rock identification key, Figure 26, determines that the name of the rock is "granite."

12. Place each of the igneous rocks supplied by your instructor on a numbered piece of paper. Then complete the igneous rock identification chart, Figure 27, for each rock. Use the igneous rock identification key, Figure 26, to determine each specimen's name.

Sedimentary Rock Identification

Sedimentary rocks, Figures 10–17, form from the accumulated products of weathering called *sediment.* Sedimentary rocks can be made of either, or a combination of, detrital or chemical material.

Detrital material consists of mineral grains or rock fragments derived from the process of mechanical weathering that are transported and deposited as solid particles (sediment). Rocks formed in this manner are called *detrital sedimentary rocks.* The mineral pieces that make

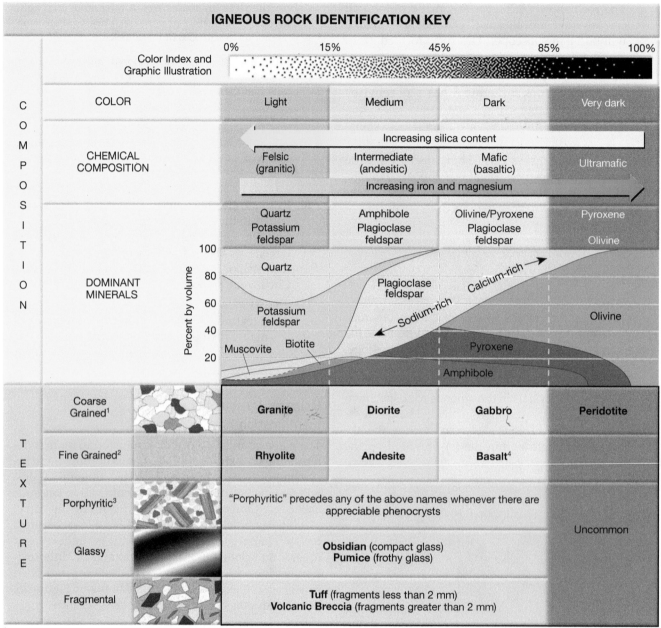

IGNEOUS ROCK IDENTIFICATION KEY

Figure 26   Igneous rock identification key. Color, with associated mineral composition, is shown along the top axis. Each rock in a column has the color and composition indicated at the top of the column. Texture is shown along the left side of the key. Each rock in a row has the texture indicated for that row. To determine the name of a rock, intersect the appropriate column (color and mineral composition) with the appropriate row (texture) and read the name at the place of intersection.

up a detrital sedimentary rock are called *grains* (or *fragments* if they are pieces of rock). The identification of a detrital sedimentary rock is determined primarily by the size of the grains or fragments. Mineral composition of the rock is a secondary concern.

Chemical material was previously dissolved in water and later precipitated by either inorganic or organic processes. Rocks formed in this manner are called *chemical sedimentary rocks*. If the material is the result of the life processes of water-dwelling organisms—for example, the formation of a shell—it is said to be of biochemical origin. Mineral composition is the primary consideration in the identification of chemical sedimentary rocks.

Sedimentary rocks come in many varieties that have formed in many different ways. For the purpose of examination, this investigation divides the sedimentary rocks into the two groups, *detrital* and *chemical*, based upon the type of material found in the rock.

Specimen Number	Texture	Color (light-intermediate-dark)	Dominant Minerals	Rock Name
I5	Coarse	L		Granite
I3	Glossy	D		Obsidian
I1	Fine	D		Basaltic
I2	Glossy	L		Pumice
I4	Fine	L		Rhyolite
I6	Fine, Grand	M		Andesite
I7	Coarse	D		Gabbro

Figure 27 Igneous rock identification chart.

Examining Sedimentary Rocks

Examine the sedimentary rock specimens supplied by your instructor. Separate those that are made of pieces or fragments of mineral, rock material, or both. They are the detrital sedimentary rocks. Do *not* include any rocks that have abundant shells or shell fragments. You may find the photographs of the detrital sedimentary rocks in Figures 10–13 helpful. The remaining sedimentary rocks, those with shells or shell fragments and those that consist of crystals, are the chemical rocks.

Pick up each detrital rock specimen and rub your finger over it to feel the size of the grains or fragments.

13. How many of your detrital specimens feel rough like sand? How many feel smooth like mud or clay?

_____ specimens feel rough and _____ feel smooth.

Use a hand lens or microscope to examine the grains or fragments of several coarse detrital rock specimens. Notice that they are not crystals.

14. Sketch the magnified pieces and surrounding material, called *cement* (or *matrix*), of a coarse detrital rock in the space provided on the following page. Indicate the scale of your sketch by writing

the appropriate length within the ( ) provided on the bar scale.

Sketch:

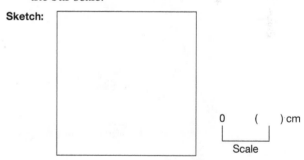

a. Observe the material surrounding the grains or fragments in the rock specimen closely with a hand lens or microscope. The material is (course, fine). Circle your answer.

b. Write a brief description of the detrital rock specimen you have examined.

_____

_____

Two of the minerals that often comprise the grains of detrital sedimentary rocks are quartz, a hard (hardness = 7) mineral with a glassy luster, and clay, a soft, fine mineral that consists of microscopic platy particles. The difference in appearance and hardness of quartz and clay is helpful in distinguishing them.

15. How many of your detrital specimens are made of quartz, and how many appear to be made of clay?

_____ specimens have quartz grains and

_____ have clay grains.

As a result of their method of formation, many chemical sedimentary rocks are fine-to-coarse crystalline, while others consist of shells or shell fragments.

16. How many of your chemical sedimentary rocks are crystalline, and how many contain abundant shells or shell fragments?

_____ specimens are crystalline and

_____ contain shells or shell fragments.

Limestones, Figures 14 and 15, are the most abundant chemical sedimentary rocks. They have several origins and many different varieties; however, one thing that all limestones have in common is that they are made of the calcium carbonate mineral called *calcite.* Calcite can precipitate directly from the sea to form limestone or can be used by marine organisms to make shells. After the organisms die, the shells become sediment and eventually the sedimentary rock limestone.

Calcite is a mineral that reacts with dilute hydrochloric acid and effervesces (fizzes) as carbon dioxide gas is released. Most limestones react readily when a small drop of acid is placed on them, thus providing a good test for identifying the rock. Many limestones also contain fragments of seashells, which also aid in their identification.

17. Follow the directions of your instructor to test the specified sedimentary rock(s) with the dilute hydrochloric acid provided and observe the results. [*Note:* Several detrital sedimentary rocks have calcite surrounding their grains or fragments (calcite cement) that will effervesce with acid and give a *false* test for limestone. Observe the acid reaction closely.]

Using a Sedimentary Rock Identification Key

The sedimentary rock identification key in Figure 28 divides the sedimentary rocks into detrital and chemical types. Notice that the primary subdivisions for the detrital rocks are based upon grain size, whereas composition is used to subdivide the chemical rocks.

Detrital Sedimentary Rocks

Texture (particle size)		Sediment Name	Rock Name
Coarse (over 2 mm)		Gravel (rounded particles)	Conglomerate
		Gravel (angular particles)	Breccia
Medium (1/16 to 2 mm)		Sand (if abundant feldspar is present the rock is called **Arkose**)	Sandstone
Fine (1/16 to 1/256 mm)		Mud	Siltstone
Very fine (less than 1/256 mm)		Mud	Shale

Chemical Sedimentary Rocks

Composition	Texture	Rock Name	
Calcite, $CaCO_3$ (effervesces in HCl)	Fine to coarse crystalline	Crystalline Limestone	
		Travertine	
	Visible shells and shell fragments loosely cemented	Coquina	Biochemical Limestone
	Various size shells and shell fragments cemented with calcite cement	Fossiliferous Limestone	
	Microscopic shells and clay	Chalk	
Quartz, SiO_2	Very fine crystalline	**Chert** (light colored) **Flint** (dark colored)	
Gypsum $CaSO_4 \bullet 2H_2O$	Fine to coarse crystalline	**Rock Gypsum**	
Halite, NaCl	Fine to coarse crystalline	**Rock Salt**	
Altered plant fragments	Fine-grained organic matter	**Bituminous Coal**	

Figure 28 Sedimentary rock identification key. Sedimentary rocks are divided into two groups, detrital and chemical, depending upon the type of material that composes them. Detrital rocks are further subdivided by the size of their grains, while the subdivision of the chemical rocks is determined by composition.

Specimen Number	Detrital or Chemical	Texture (grain size)	Sediment Name or Composition	Rock Name
S5	C	Fine	Altered plant	Coal
S1	D	very fine	Mud	Shale
S2	D	coarse	Gravel	Conglomerate
S3	D	Medium	Sand	Sandstone
S4	C	coarse	Calcite	Coquina

Figure 29 Sedimentary rock identification chart.

18. Place each of the sedimentary rocks supplied by your instructor on a numbered piece of paper. Then complete the sedimentary rock identification chart, Figure 29, for each rock. Use the sedimentary rock identification key, Figure 28, to determine each specimen's name.

Sedimentary Rocks and Environments

Sedimentary rocks are extremely important in the study of Earth's history. Particle size and the materials from which they are made often suggest something about the place, or environment, in which the rock formed. The fossils that often are found in a sedimentary rock also provide information about the rock's history.

Reexamine the sedimentary rocks and think of them as representing a "place" on Earth where the sediment was deposited.

19. Figure 11 is the rock sandstone that formed from sand. Where on Earth do you find sand, the primary material of sandstone, being deposited today?

_____

Figure 30 shows a few generalized environments (places) where sediment accumulates. Often, an environment is characterized by the type of sediment and life forms associated with it.

20. Use Figure 30 to name the environment(s) where, in the past, the sediment for the following sedimentary rocks may have been deposited.

ORIGINAL SEDIMENT		ENVIRONMENT(S)
Sandstone:	(sand)	
Shale:	(mud)	
Limestone:	(coral, shells)	

Metamorphic Rock Identification

Metamorphic rocks were previously igneous, sedimentary, or other metamorphic rocks that were changed by any combination of heat, pressure, and chemical fluids during the process of **metamorphism**. They are most often located beneath sedimentary rocks on the continents and in the cores of mountains.

During metamorphism new minerals may form, and/or existing minerals can grow larger as metamorphism becomes more intense. Frequently, mineral crystals that are elongated (like hornblende) or have a sheet structure (like the micas—biotite and muscovite) become oriented perpendicular to compressional forces. The resulting parallel, linear alignment of mineral crystals perpendicular to compressional forces (differential stress) is called **foliation** (Figure 31). Foliation is unique to many metamorphic rocks and gives them a layered or banded appearance.

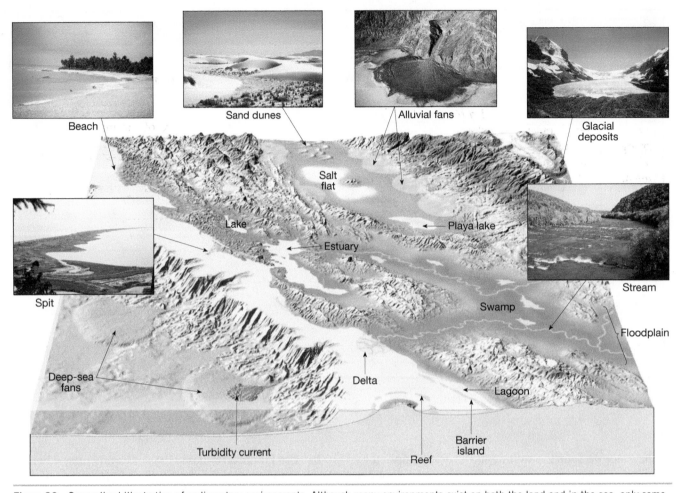

Figure 30 Generalized illustration of sedimentary environments. Although many environments exist on both the land and in the sea, only some of the most important are represented in this idealized diagram. (Photos by E. J. Tarbuck, except alluvial fan, by Marli Miller)

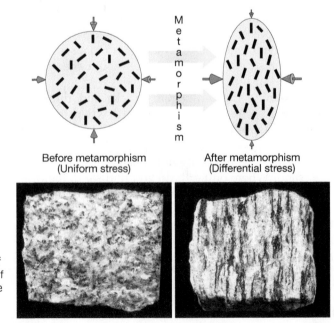

Figure 31 Under directed pressure, planar minerals, such as the micas, become reoriented or recrystallized so that their surfaces are aligned at right angles to the stress. The resulting planar orientation of mineral grains is called **foliation** and gives the rock a foliated texture. If the coarse-grained igneous rock (granite) on the left underwent intense metamorphism, it could end up closely resembling the metamorphic rock on the right (gneiss). (Photos by E. J. Tarbuck)

Metamorphic rocks are divided into two groups based on texture—foliated and nonfoliated. These textural divisions provide the basis for the identification of metamorphic rocks.

Foliated Metamorphic Rocks

The mineral crystals in foliated metamorphic rocks are either elongated or have a sheet structure and are arranged in a parallel or "layered" manner. *During metamorphism, increased heat and pressure can cause the mineral crystals to become larger and the foliation more obvious.* (Figure 32) The metamorphic rocks in Figures 18–22 exhibit foliated textures.

21. From the rocks illustrated in Figures 18 and 20, the (slate, schist) resulted from more intensive heat and pressure. Circle your answer.

22. From the metamorphic rocks in Figures 19 and 21, the (phyllite, gneiss) shows the minerals separated into light and dark bands. Circle your answer. (The foliated-banded texture of the rock that you have selected often results from the most intensive heat and pressure during metamorphism.)

Select several of the foliated metamorphic rock specimens supplied by your instructor that have large crystals and examine them with a hand lens or microscope.

23. Sketch the appearance of the magnified crystals of one foliated metamorphic rock in the space provided below. Indicate the scale of your sketch by writing the appropriate length within the ( ) provided on the bar scale.

Sketch:

0   (   ) cm

Scale

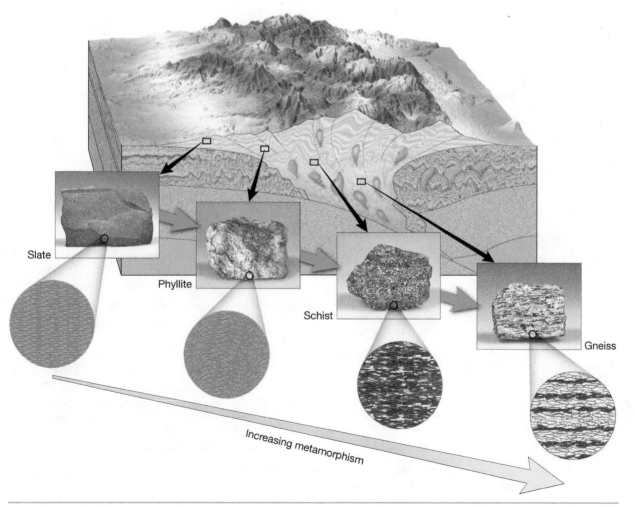

Figure 32 Idealized illustration showing the effect of increasing metamorphism in foliated metamorphic rocks. (Photos by E. J. Tarbuck)

Nonfoliated Metamorphic Rocks

Nonfoliated metamorphic rocks are most often identified by determining their mineral composition. The minerals that comprise them, most often calcite or quartz, are neither elongated nor sheet structured and therefore cannot be as easily aligned. Hence, no foliation develops during metamorphism.

24. Examine the nonfoliated metamorphic rocks supplied by your instructor to determine if any are composed of calcite or quartz. Hardness and the reaction to dilute hydrochloric acid often provide a clue.

CAUTION: Follow the directions of your instructor when using acid to test for calcite.

Using a Metamorphic Rock Identification Key

A metamorphic rock identification key is presented in Figure 33. To use the key, first determine a rock's texture, foliated or nonfoliated, and then proceed to further

subdivisions to arrive at a name. The names of the medium or coarse foliated rocks are often modified with the mineral composition placed in front of the name (e.g., "mica schist").

25. Place each of the metamorphic rocks supplied by your instructor on a numbered piece of paper. Then complete the metamorphic rock identification chart, Figure 34, for each rock. Use the metamorphic rock identification key, Figure 33 to determine each specimen's name.

Rocks on the Internet

Associated with igneous rock, the most abundant rock on Earth, are often geologic hazards related to volcanic activity. Investigate this potentially destructive geologic process by completing the corresponding online activity on the *Applications & Investigations in Earth Science* website at http://prenhall.com/earthsciencelab

Texture	Grain Size	Rock Name	Comments	Parent Rock
Foliated	Very fine	Slate	Excellent rock cleavage, smooth dull surfaces	Shale, mudstone, or siltstone
Foliated	Fine	Phyllite	Breaks along wavey surfaces, glossy sheen	Slate
Foliated	Medium to Coarse	Schist	Micas dominate, scaly foliation	Phyllite
Foliated	Medium to Coarse	Gneiss	Compositional banding due to segregation of minerals	Schist, granite, or volcanic rocks
Nonfoliated	Medium to coarse	Marble	Interlocking calcite or dolomite grains	Limestone, dolostone
Nonfoliated	Medium to coarse	Quartzite	Fused quartz grains, massive, very hard	Quartz sandstone
Nonfoliated	Fine	Anthracite	Shiny black organic rock that may exhibit conchoidal fracture	Bituminous coal

(Increasing Metamorphism)

Figure 33 Metamorphic rock identification key. Metamorphic rocks are divided into the two textual groups, foliated and nonfoliated. Foliated rocks are further subdivided based upon the size of the mineral grains.

Specimen Number	Foliated or Nonfoliated	Grain Size	Composition (if identifiable)	Rock Name
M4	F	Very fine	Smooth dull surface	Slate
M5	N	Fine	Shiny black organic	Anthracite
M1	N	Coarse	dolomite grains	Marble
M3	F	Coarse		Gneiss
M2	F	Coarse	Mica dominate	schist

Figure 34   Metamorphic rock identification chart.

Notes and calculations.

Common Rocks

Date Due: _____

Name: _____

Date: _____

Class: _____

After you have finished this exercise, complete the following questions. You may have to refer to the exercise for assistance or to locate specific answers. Be prepared to submit this summary/report to your instructor at the designated time.

1. Write a brief definition of each of the three rock types.

    Igneous rocks: _____

    _____

    _____

    Sedimentary rocks: _____

    _____

    _____

    Metamorphic rocks: _____

    _____

    _____

2. What unique factor about the arrangement of mineral crystals occurs in many metamorphic rocks?

    _____

3. Describe the procedure you would follow to determine the name of a specific igneous rock.

    _____

    _____

    _____

4. Describe the basic difference between detrital and chemical sedimentary rocks.

    _____

    _____

5. List the *texture* and mineral *composition* of each of the following rocks.

	TEXTURE	MINERAL COMPOSITION
Granite:	_____	_____
Marble:	_____	_____
Sandstone:	_____	_____

6. What are two possible environments for the origin of the sedimentary rock sandstone?

    _____

    _____

    _____

7. Of the three rock types, which one is most likely to contain fossils? Explain the reason for your choice.

    _____

    _____

    _____

8. What factor determines the size of the crystals in igneous rocks?

    _____

9. What is a good chemical test to determine the primary mineral in limestone?

    _____

10. What factor(s) determine(s) the size of crystals in metamorphic rocks?

    _____

    _____

33

11. If the sedimentary rock limestone is subjected to metamorphism, what metamorphic rock will likely form?

_____

12. With reference to the rock cycle, describe the processes and changes that an igneous rock will undergo as it is changed first to a sedimentary rock, which then becomes a metamorphic rock.

_____

_____

_____

13. Select two igneous, two sedimentary, and two metamorphic rocks that you identified, and write a brief description of each.

Rock type: _____

Rock name: _____

Description: _____

_____

Rock type: _____

Rock name: _____

Description: _____

_____

Rock type: _____

Rock name: _____

Description: _____

_____

Rock type: _____

Rock name: _____

Description: _____

_____

Rock type: _____

Rock name: _____

Description: _____

_____

_____

Rock type: _____

Rock name: _____

Description: _____

_____

14. Referring to Figure 35, list each rock's name and write a brief description of each.

A: _____

_____

_____

B: _____

_____

_____

C: _____

_____

_____

Figure 35 Three rock specimens for use with question 14.

34

Determining Geologic Ages

The recognition of the vastness of geologic time and the ability to establish the sequence of geologic events that have occurred at various places at different times are among the great intellectual achievements of science. To accomplish the task of deciphering Earth's history, geologists have formulated several laws, principles, and doctrines that can be used to place geologic events in their proper sequence (Figure 1). Also, using the principles that govern the radioactive decay of certain elements, scientists are now able to determine the age of many Earth materials with reasonable accuracy. In this exercise you will investigate some of the techniques and procedures used by Earth scientists in their search to interpret the geologic history of Earth.

Objectives

After you have completed this exercise, you should be able to:

1. List and explain each of the laws, principles, and doctrines that are used to determine the relative ages of geologic events.
2. Determine the sequence of geologic events that have occurred in an area by applying the techniques and procedures for relative dating.
3. Explain the methods of fossilization and how fossils are used to define the ages of rocks and correlate rock units.
4. Explain how the radioactive decay of certain elements can be used to determine the age of Earth materials.
5. Apply the techniques of radiometric dating to determine the numerical age of a rock.
6. Describe the geologic time scale and list in proper order some of the major events that have taken place on Earth since its formation.

Figure 1 In any sequence of underformed sedimentary rocks, the oldest rock is always at the bottom and the youngest is at the top. (Photo by E. J. Tarbuck)

Materials

ruler   calculator

Materials Supplied by Your Instructor

fossils and fossil questions   meterstick or metric
  (optional)   tape measure
5-meter length of adding-
  machine paper

Terms

relative dating   unconformity   radiometric
uniformitarianism cross-cutting   date
original   fossil   half-life
  horizontality   fossil succession   eon
superposition   era
inclusion

From *Applications and Investigations in Earth Science,* Sixth Edition, Edward J. Tarbuck, Frederick K. Lutgens, Kenneth G. Pinzke. Copyright © 2009 by Pearson Education, Inc. Published by Pearson Prentice Hall. All rights reserved.

Relative Dating

Relative dating, the placing of geologic events in their proper sequence or order, does not tell how long ago something occurred, only that it preceded one event and followed another. Several logical doctrines, laws, and principles govern the techniques used to establish the relative age of an object or event.

Doctrine of Uniformitarianism

First proposed by James Hutton in the late 1700s, this doctrine states that the physical, chemical, and biological laws that operate today have operated throughout Earth's history. Although geologic processes such as erosion, deposition, and volcanism are governed by these unchanging laws, their rates and intensities may vary. The doctrine is often summarized in the statement, "The present is the key to the past."

Principle of Original Horizontality

Sediment, when deposited, forms nearly horizontal layers. Therefore, if we observe beds of sedimentary rocks that are folded or inclined at a steep angle, the implication is that some deforming force took place after the sediment was deposited (Figure 2).

Law of Superposition

In any sequence of undeformed sedimentary rocks (or surface deposited igneous rocks such as lava flows and layers of volcanic ash), the oldest rock is always at the bottom and the youngest is at the top. Therefore, each layer of rock represents an interval of time that is more recent than that of the underlying rocks (see Figure 1).

Figure 2 Uplifted and tilted sedimentary strata in the Canadian Rockies. (Photo by E. J. Tarbuck)

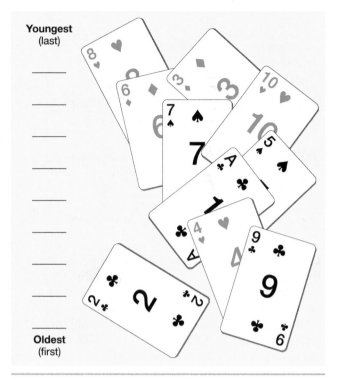

Youngest
(last)

Oldest
(first)

Figure 3 Sequence of playing cards illustrating the law of superposition.

Assume the playing cards shown in Figure 3 are layers of sedimentary rocks viewed from above.

1. In the space provided in Figure 3, list the order, first (oldest) to last (youngest), in which the cards were laid down.

2. Were you able to place all of the cards in sequence? If not, which one(s) could not be "relative" dated and why?

_____

_____

Figure 4 illustrates a geologic cross section, a side view, of the rocks beneath the surface of a hypothetical region. Use Figure 4 to answer questions 3 and 4.

3. Of the two sequences of rocks, A–D and E–G (A–D, E–G), was disturbed by crustal movements after its deposition. Circle your answer. What law or principle did you apply to arrive at your answer?

_____

4. Apply the law of superposition to determine the relative ages of the *undisturbed* sequence of sedimentary rocks. List the letter of the oldest rock layer first.

Oldest _____ Youngest

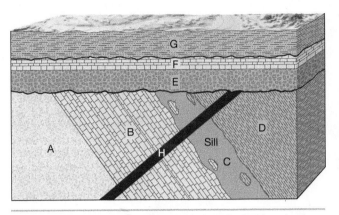

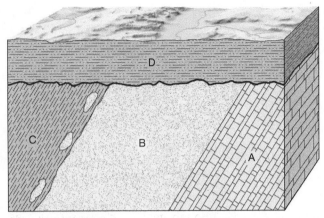

Figure 4 Geologic block diagram of a hypothetical region showing igneous intrusive features (C and H) and sedimentary rocks.

Figure 6 Geologic block diagram showing sedimentary rocks.

Inclusions

Inclusions are pieces of one rock unit that are contained within another unit (Figure 5). The rock mass adjacent to the one containing the inclusions must have been there first in order to provide the rock fragments. Therefore, the rock containing the inclusions is the younger of the two.

Refer to Figure 6 to answer questions 5 and 6. The sedimentary layer B is a sandstone. Letter C is the sedimentary rock, shale.

5. Identify and label the inclusions in Figure 6.
6. Of the two rocks B and C, rock (B, C) is older. Circle your answer.

Unconformities

As long as continuous sedimentation occurs at a particular place, there will be an uninterrupted record of the material and life forms. However, if the sedimentation process is suspended by an emergence of the area from below sea level, then no sediment will be deposited and

an erosion surface will develop. The result is that no rock record will exist for a part of geologic time. Such a gap in the rock record is termed an **unconformity**. An unconformity is typically shown on a cross-sectional (side view) diagram by a wavy line (∿∿). Several types of unconformities are illustrated in Figure 7.

7. Identify and label an example of an angular unconformity and a disconformity in Figure 4.

Principle of Cross-Cutting Relationships

Whenever a fault or intrusive igneous rock cuts through an existing feature, it is younger than the structure it cuts. For example, if a basalt dike cuts through a sandstone layer, the sandstone had to be there first and, therefore, is older than the dike (Figure 8).

Figure 9 is a geologic cross section showing sedimentary rocks (A, B, D, E, F, and G), an igneous intrusive feature called a *dike* (C), and a *fault* (H). Use Figure 9 to answer questions 8–11.

8. The igneous intrusion C is (older, younger) than the sedimentary rocks B and D. Circle your answer.
9. Fault H is (older, younger) than the sedimentary beds A–E.
10. The relative age of fault H is (older, younger) than the sedimentary layer F.
11. Did the fault occur before or after the igneous intrusion? Explain how you arrived at your answer.

_____

_____

12. Refer to Figure 4. The igneous intrusion H is (older, younger) than rock layer E and (older, younger) than layer D. Circle your answers.
13. Refer to Figure 4. What evidence supports the conclusion that the igneous intrusive feature

Figure 5 Inclusions are fragments of one rock enclosed within another. (Photo by E. J. Tarbuck)

37

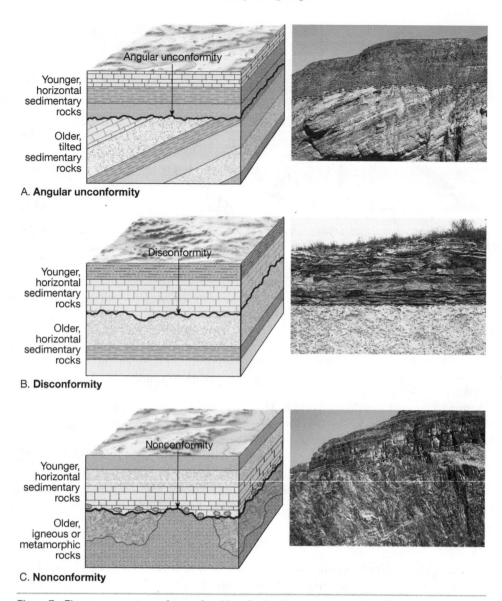

Figure 7 Three common types of unconformities. On the diagrams, wavy dashed lines mark the unconformity.

A. **Angular unconformity**

B. **Disconformity**

C. **Nonconformity**

Figure 8 This basalt dike (black) is younger than the sandstone layers that it cuts through. (Photo by E. J. Tarbuck)

called a *sill*, C, is more recent than both of the rock layers B and D and older than the igneous intrusion H?

Fossils and the Principle of Fossil Succession

Fossils (Figure 10) are among the most important tools used to interpret Earth's history. They are used to define the ages of rocks, correlate one rock unit with another, and determine past environments on Earth.

Earth has been inhabited by different assemblages of plants and animals at different times. As rocks form, they often incorporate the preserved remains of these organisms as fossils. According to the principle of **fossil succession**, fossil organisms succeed each other in a definite and determinable order. Therefore, the time that a rock originated can frequently be determined by noting the kinds of fossils that are found within it.

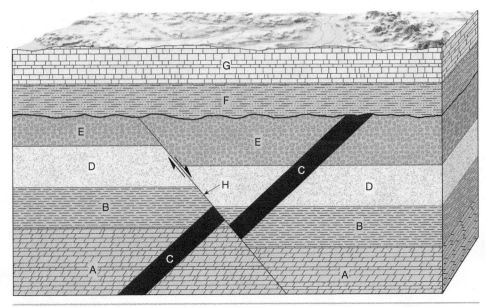

Figure 9 Geologic block diagram of a hypothetical area showing an igneous intrusion (C), a fault (H), and sedimentary rocks.

A.

B.

C.

D.

Figure 10 Various types of fossilization. In photo **A.** the mineral quartz now occupies the internal spaces of what was once wood. **B.** is the replica of fish after the carbonized remains were removed. In photo **C.** mineral matter occupies the hollow space where a shell was once located. **D.** is a track left by a dinosaur in formerly soft sediment. (Photos by E. J. Tarbuck)

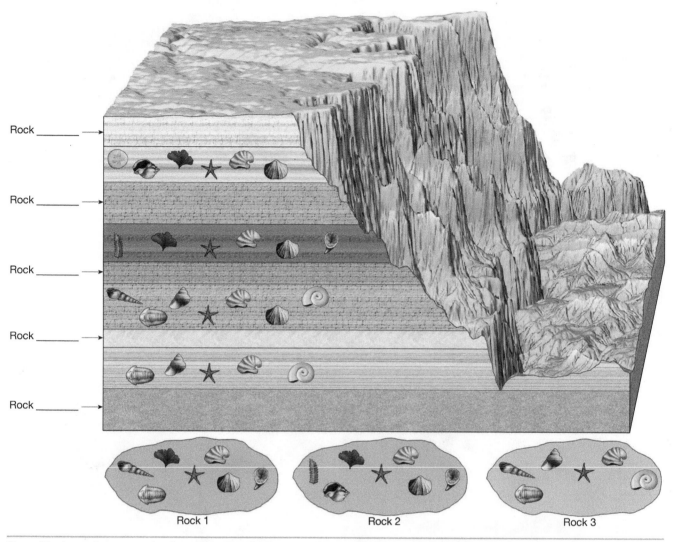

Rock _____

Rock _____

Rock _____

Rock _____

Rock _____

Rock 1   Rock 2   Rock 3

Figure 11   Layered sequence of sedimentary rocks with fossils and three separate rocks containing similar fossils.

Using the materials supplied by your instructor, answer questions 14 and 15.

14. At the discretion of your instructor, there may be several stations with fossils and questions set up in the laboratory. Following the specific directions of your instructor, proceed to the stations.

15. What are the conditions that would favor the preservation of an organism as a fossil?

_____

_____

16. Refer to Figure 10. Select the photo, A, B, C, or D, that best illustrates each of the following methods of fossilization or fossil evidence.

    Petrification: The small internal cavities and pores of the original organism are filled with precipitated mineral matter. Photo: _____

Cast: The space once occupied by a dissolved shell or other structure is subsequently filled with mineral matter. Photo: _____

Impression: A replica of a former fossil left in fine-grained sediment after the fossilizing material, often carbon, is removed. Photo: _____

Indirect evidence: Traces of prehistoric life, but not the organism itself. Photo: _____

Figure 11 shows a sequence of undeformed sedimentary rocks. Each layer of rock contains the fossils illustrated within it. The three rocks, Rocks 1, 2, and 3, illustrated below the layered sequence were found nearby and each rock contains the fossils indicated. Answer question 17 using Figure 11.

17. Applying the principle of fossil succession, indicate the proper position of each of the three rocks relative to the rock layers by writing the words Rock 1, Rock 2, or Rock 3 at the appropriate position in the sequence.

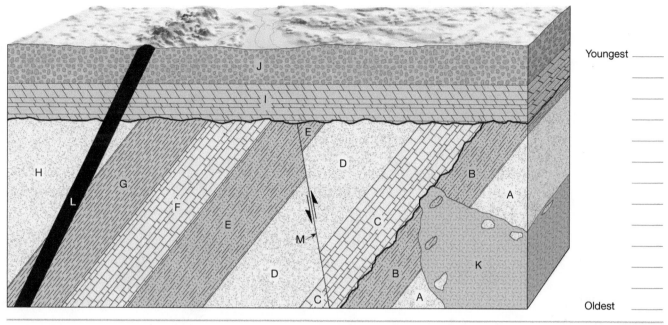

Youngest _____

_____

_____

_____

_____

_____

_____

_____

_____

_____

_____

Oldest _____

Figure 12 Geologic block diagram of a hypothetical area showing igneous intrusive features (K and L), a fault (M), and sedimentary rocks.

Applying Relative Dating Techniques

Geologists often apply several of the techniques of relative dating when investigating the geologic history of an area.

Figure 12 is a geologic cross section of a hypothetical area. Letters K and L are igneous rocks. Letter M is a fault. All the remaining letters represent sedimentary rocks. Using Figure 12 to complete questions 18–24 will provide insight into how the relative geologic history of an area is determined.

18. Identify and label the unconformities indicated in the cross section.

19. Rock layer I is (older, younger) than layer J. Circle your answer. What law or principle have you applied to determine your answer?

_____

_____

20. The fault is (older, younger) than rock layer I. Circle your answer. What law or principle have you applied to determine your answer?

_____

_____

21. The igneous intrusion K is (older, younger) than layers A and B. Circle your answer. What two laws or principles have you applied to determine your answer?

_____ and _____

22. The age of the igneous intrusion L is (older, younger) than layers J, I, H, G, and F.

23. List the entire sequence of events, in order from oldest to youngest, by writing the appropriate letter in the space provided on the figure.

24. Explain why it was difficult to place the fault, letter M, in a specific position among the sequence of events in Figure 12.

_____

_____

_____

_____

_____

_____

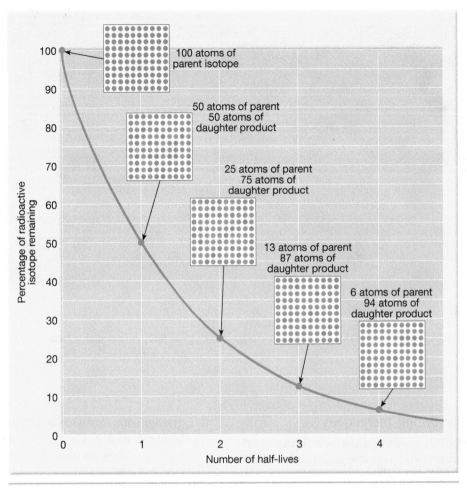

Figure 13 Radioactive decay curve.

Radiometric Dating

The discovery of radioactivity and its subsequent understanding has provided a reliable means for calculating the *numerical age* in years of many Earth materials. Radioactive atoms, such as the isotope uranium-238, emit particles from their nuclei that we detect as radiation. Ultimately, this process of decay produces an atom that is stable and no longer radioactive. For example, eventually the stable atom lead-206 is produced from the radioactive decay of uranium-238.

Determining Radiometric Ages

The radioactive isotope used to determine a **radiometric date** is referred to as the *parent isotope*. The amount of time it takes for half of the radioactive nuclei in a sample to change to their stable end product is referred to as the **half-life** of the isotope. The isotopes resulting from the decay of the parent are termed the *daughter products*. For example, if we begin with one gram of radioactive material, half a gram would decay and become a daughter product after one half-life. After the second half-life, half

of the remaining radioactive isotope, 0.25 g or $\frac{1}{4}$ of the original amount $\left(\frac{1}{2} \text{ of } \frac{1}{2}\right)$, would still exist. *With each successive half-life, the remaining parent isotope would be reduced by half.*

Figure 13 graphically illustrates how the ratio of a parent isotope to its stable daughter product continually changes with time. Use Figure 13 to help answer questions 25–29.

25. What percentage of the original parent isotope remains after each of the following half-lives has elapsed?

	FRACTION OF PARENT ISOTOPE REMAINING
One half-life:	_____
Two half-lives:	_____
Three half-lives:	_____
Four half-lives:	_____

26. Assume you begin with 10.0 g of a radioactive parent isotope. How many grams of parent isotope will be present in the sample after each of the following half-lives?

REMAINING PARENT ISOTOPE

One half-life: _____ g

Four half-lives: _____ g

27. If a radioactive isotope has a half-life of 400 million years, how long will it take for 50% of the material to change to the daughter product?

_____ years

28. A sample is brought to the laboratory and the chemist determines that the percentage of the parent isotope remaining is 13% of the total amount that was originally present. If the half-life of the material is 600 million years, how old is the sample?

_____ years old

29. Determine the numerical ages of rock samples that contain a parent isotope with a half-life of 100 million years and have the following percentages of original parent isotope.

50%: Age = _____

25%: Age = _____

6%: Age = _____

Applying Radiometric Dates

When used in conjunction with relative dates, radiometric dates help Earth scientists refine their interpretation of the geologic history of an area. Completing questions 30–35 will aid in understanding how both types of dates are often used together.

Previously in the exercise you determined the geologic history of the area represented in Figure 12 using relative dating techniques. Assume that the rock layers H and I in Figure 12 each contain radioactive materials with known half-lives.

30. An analysis of a sample of rock from layer H indicates an equal proportion of parent isotope and daughter produced from the parent. The half-life of the parent is known to be 425 million years.

   a. (Fifty, Twenty-five, Thirteen) percent of the original parent has decayed to the daughter product. Circle your answer.

   b. How many half-lives of the parent isotope have elapsed since rock H formed?

   _____

   c. What is the numerical age of rock layer H? Write your answer below and at rock layer H on Figure 12.

   Age of rock layer H = _____ years

31. The analysis of a sample of rock from layer I indicates its age to be 400 million years. Write the numerical age of layer I on Figure 12.

Refer to the relative and numerical ages you determined for the rocks in Figure 12 to answer the following questions.

32. How many years long is the interval of time represented by the unconformity that separates rock layer H from layer I? Explain how you arrived at your answer.

The unconformity represents an interval of time that was _____ million years long.

Explanation: _____

_____

_____

_____

33. The age of fault M is (older, younger) than 400 million years. Circle your answer. Explain how you arrived at your answer.

Explanation: _____

_____

_____

_____

34. What is the approximate maximum numerical age of the igneous intrusion L?

The igneous intrusion L formed more recently than _____ million years ago.

35. Complete the following general statement describing the numerical ages of rock layers G, F, and E.

All of the rock layers are (younger, older) than _____ million years.

The Geologic Time Scale

Applying the techniques of geologic dating, the history of Earth has been subdivided into several different units which provide a meaningful time frame within which the events of the geologic past are arranged. Since the span of a human life is but a "blink of an eye" compared to the age of Earth, it is often difficult to comprehend the magnitude of geologic time. By completing questions 36–41, you will be better able to grasp the great age of Earth and appreciate the sequence of events that have brought it to this point in time.

36. Obtain a piece of adding machine paper slightly longer than 5 meters and a meterstick or metric measuring tape from your instructor. Draw a line at one end of the paper and label it "PRESENT." Using the following scale, construct a time line by completing the indicated steps.

SCALE

1 meter = 1 billion years

10 centimeters = 100 million years

1 centimeter = 10 million years

1 millimeter = 1 million years

Step 1. Using the geologic time scale, Figure 14, as a reference, divide your time line into the **eons** and **eras** of geologic time. Label each division with its name and indicate its absolute age.

Step 2. Using the scale, plot and label the plant and animal events listed in Figure 14 on your time line.

After completing your time line, answer questions 37–41.

37. What fraction or percent of geologic time is represented by the Precambrian eon?

Approximately _____ of geologic time.

38. Suggest a reason(s) why approximately 542 million years ago was selected to mark the end of Proterozoic eon and the beginning of the Paleozoic era.

_____

39. Write a brief statement outlining the various life forms that have existed on Earth through time.

_____

_____

_____

40. How many times longer is the whole of geologic time than the time represented by recorded history, about 5,000 years?

Geologic time is _____ times longer than recorded history.

41. For what fraction or percent of geologic time have land plants been present on Earth?

Approximately _____ of geologic time.

Geologic Time on the Internet

Apply what you have learned in this exercise to write a geologic interpretation of a rock outcrop and to explore the fossil record by completing the corresponding online activities on the *Applications & Investigations in Earth Science* website at http://prenhall.com/earthsciencelab

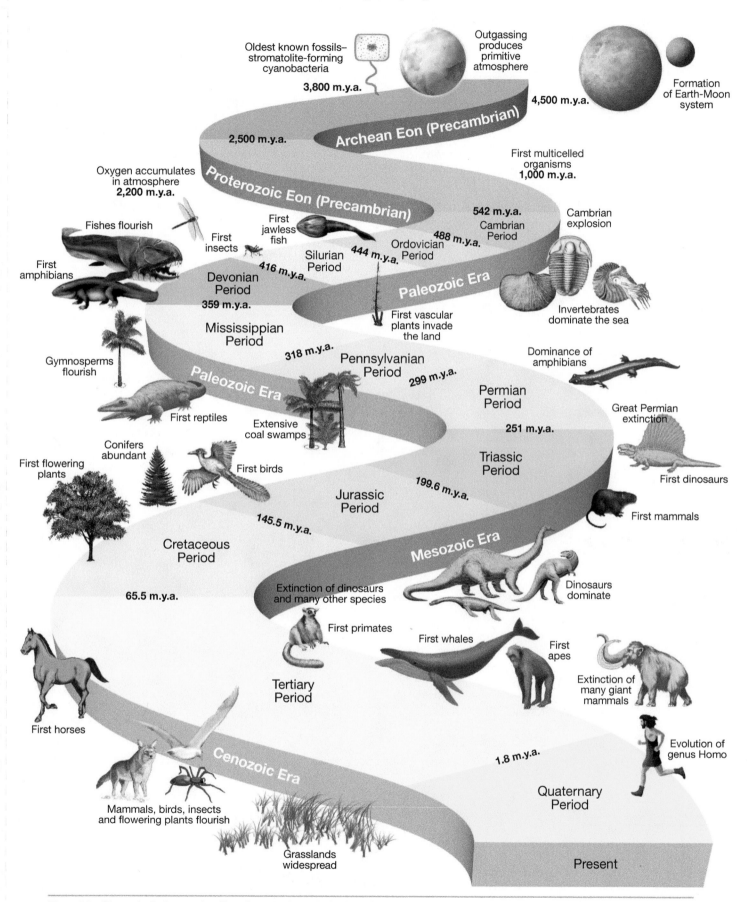

Oldest known fossils–
stromatolite-forming
cyanobacteria
3,800 m.y.a.

Outgassing
produces
primitive
atmosphere

4,500 m.y.a.

Formation
of Earth-Moon
system

Archean Eon (Precambrian)

2,500 m.y.a.

Oxygen accumulates
in atmosphere
2,200 m.y.a.

Proterozoic Eon (Precambrian)

First multicelled
organisms
1,000 m.y.a.

First
jawless
fish

First
insects

542 m.y.a.
Cambrian
Period

Cambrian
explosion

488 m.y.a.
Ordovician
Period

Silurian
Period
444 m.y.a.

Paleozoic Era

Fishes flourish

First
amphibians

Devonian
Period
416 m.y.a.

359 m.y.a.

First vascular
plants invade
the land

Invertebrates
dominate the sea

Mississippian
Period

Gymnosperms
flourish

318 m.y.a.

Pennsylvanian
Period

Paleozoic Era

299 m.y.a.

Dominance of
amphibians

First reptiles

Extensive
coal swamps

Permian
Period

251 m.y.a.

Great Permian
extinction

Conifers
abundant

First flowering
plants

First birds

Triassic
Period

199.6 m.y.a.

First dinosaurs

Jurassic
Period

First mammals

145.5 m.y.a.

Cretaceous
Period

Mesozoic Era

65.5 m.y.a.

Extinction of dinosaurs
and many other species

Dinosaurs
dominate

First primates

First whales

First
apes

Extinction of
many giant
mammals

First horses

Tertiary
Period

Cenozoic Era

1.8 m.y.a.

Evolution of
genus Homo

Quaternary
Period

Mammals, birds, insects
and flowering plants flourish

Grasslands
widespread

Present

Figure 14 The geologic time scale. (Data from the Geologic Society of America)

Notes and calculations.

Determining Geologic Ages

Date Due: _____

Name: _____

Date: _____

Class: _____

After you have finished this exercise, complete the following questions. You may have to refer to the exercise for assistance or to locate specific answers. Be prepared to submit this summary/report to your instructor at the designated time.

1. Determine the sequence of geologic events that have occurred at the hypothetical area illustrated in Figure 15. List your answers from oldest to youngest in the space provided by the figure. Letters M and N are faults, J, K, and L are igneous intrusions, and all other layers are sedimentary rocks.

2. The following questions refer to Figure 15.

    a. What type of unconformity separates layer G from layer F?

    _____

    b. Which law, principle, or doctrine of relative dating did you apply to determine that rock layer H is older than layer I?

    _____

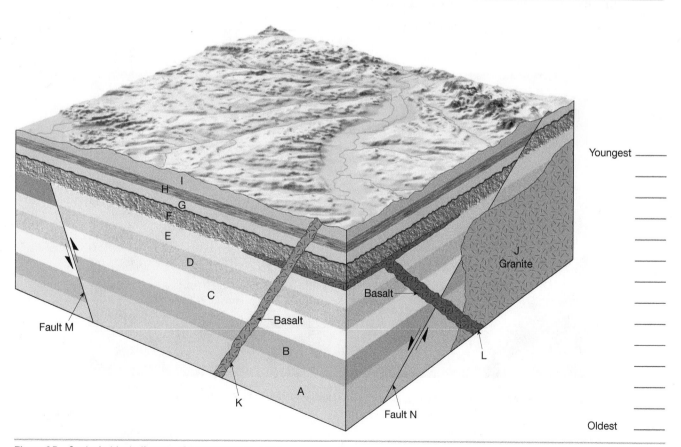

Figure 15 Geologic block diagram of a hypothetical region.

47

c. Which law, principle, or doctrine of relative dating did you apply to determine that fault M is older than rock layer F?

_____

d. Explain why you know that fault N is older than the igneous intrusion J.

_____

e. If rock layer F is 150 million years old and layer E is 160 million years old, what is the approximate age of fault M?

_____ million years

f. The analysis of samples from layers G and F indicates the following proportions of parent isotope to the daughter product produced from it. If the half-life of the parent is known to be 75 million years, what are the ages of the two layers?

	PARENT	DAUGHTER	AGE
Layer G:	50%	50%	_____
Layer F:	25%	75%	_____

g. What absolute time interval is represented by the unconformity at the base of rock layer G?

From _____ to _____ million years

3. List the sequence of geologic events that you determined took place in the area represented by Figure 12, question 23, in the exercise.

Oldest _____ Youngest

4. What fraction of time is represented by each of the following geologic eons?

Phanerozoic eon: _____ Precambrian eon: _____

5. How many meters long would the time line you constructed in the exercise, question 36, have been if you had used a scale of 1 millimeter equals 1,000 years?

_____

6. Examine the photograph in Figure 16 closely. Applying the principles of relative dating, describe as accurately as possible the relative geologic history of the area.

_____

_____

_____

_____

Figure 16   Photo of sedimentary beds to be used with question 6. (Photo by E. J. Tarbuck)

Earthquakes and Earth's Interior

Almost all of Earth lies beneath us, yet its accessibility to direct examination is limited. Therefore, one of the most difficult problems faced by Earth scientists is determining the physical properties of Earth's interior. The branch of Earth science called **seismology** combines mathematics and physics to explain the nature of earthquakes and how they can be used to gather information about Earth beyond our view. This exercise introduces some of the techniques that are used by seismologists to determine the location of an earthquake and to investigate the structure of Earth's interior.

Objectives

After you have completed this exercise, you should be able to:

1. Examine an earthquake seismogram and recognize the P waves, S waves, and surface waves.

2. Use a seismogram and travel-time graph to determine how far a seismic station is from the epicenter of an earthquake.

3. Determine the actual time that an earthquake occurred using a seismogram and travel-time graph.

4. Locate the epicenter of an earthquake by plotting seismic data from three seismic stations.

5. Explain how earthquakes are used to determine the structure of Earth's interior.

6. List the name, depth, composition, and state of matter of each of Earth's interior zones.

7. Describe the temperature gradient of the upper Earth.

8. Explain why Earth scientists think that the asthenosphere consists of partly melted, plastic material at a depth of about 100 kilometers.

9. Explain how earthquakes and Earth's temperature gradient have been used to explain the fact that large, rigid slabs of the lithosphere are descending into the mantle at various locations on Earth.

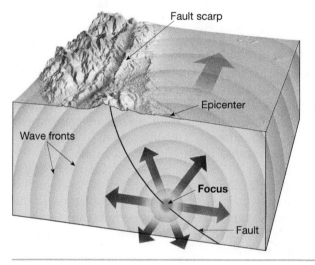

Figure 1 Earthquake focus and epicenter. The focus is the zone within Earth where the initial displacement occurs. The epicenter is the surface location directly above the focus.

Materials

calculator	colored pencils
drawing compass	ruler

Materials Supplied by Your Instructor

atlas or wall map

Terms

seismology	P wave	asthenosphere
lithosphere	S wave	mantle
focus	surface wave	outer core
seismic wave	amplitude	inner core
seismograph	period	geothermal gradient
seismogram	epicenter	

Earthquakes

Earthquakes are vibrations of Earth that occur when the rigid materials of the **lithosphere** are strained beyond their limit, yield, and "spring back" to their original shape, rapidly releasing stored energy. This energy radiates in all directions from the source of the earthquake, called the **focus**, in the form of **seismic waves**. (Figure 1). **Seismograph** instruments (Figure 2) located throughout the world amplify and record the ground motions produced by passing seismic waves on **seismograms** (Figure 3). The seismograms are then used to determine the time of occurrence and location of an earthquake, as well as to define the internal structure of Earth.

Examining Seismograms

The three basic types of seismic waves generated by an earthquake at its focus are **P waves**, **S waves**, and **surface waves** (Figure 4). P and S waves travel through Earth while surface waves are transmitted along the outer layer. Of the three wave types, P waves have the greatest velocity and, therefore, reach the seismograph station first. Surface waves arrive at the seismograph station last. P waves also have smaller **amplitudes** (range from the mean, or average, to the extreme) (Figure 3) and shorter **periods** (time interval between the arrival of successive wave crests) than S and surface waves.

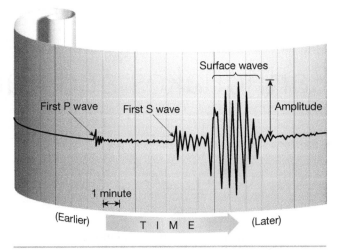

Figure 3 Typical earthquake seismogram.

On Figure 3, a typical earthquake recording on a seismogram, each vertical line marks a one-minute time interval. Answer questions 1–6 by referring to Figure 3.

1. It took approximately (5, 7, 11) minutes to record the entire earthquake from the first recording of the P waves to the end of the surface waves. Circle your answer.

2. (Five, Seven) minutes elapsed between the arrival of the first P wave and the arrival of the first S wave on the seismogram. Circle your answer.

3. (Five, Seven) minutes elapsed between the arrival of the first P wave and the first surface wave.

4. The maximum amplitude of the surface waves is approximately (5, 9) times greater than the maximum amplitude of the P waves.

5. The approximate period of the surface waves is (10, 30, 60) seconds.

6. The period of the surface waves is (greater, less) than the period for P waves.

Locating an Earthquake

The focus of an earthquake is the actual place within Earth where the earthquake originates. Earthquake foci have been recorded to depths as great as 600 km. When locating an earthquake on a map, seismologists plot the **epicenter**, the point on Earth's surface directly above the focus (Figure 1).

The difference in the velocities of P and S waves provides a method for locating the epicenter of an earthquake. Both P and S waves leave the earthquake focus at the same instant. Since the P wave has a greater velocity, the further away the recording instrument is from the focus, the greater will be the difference in the arrival times of the first P wave compared to the first S wave.

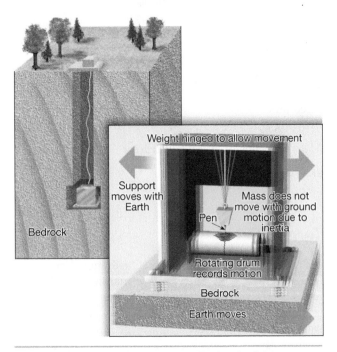

Figure 2 Principle of the seismograph. The inertia of the suspended mass tends to keep it motionless, while the recording drum, which is anchored to bedrock, vibrates in response to seismic waves.

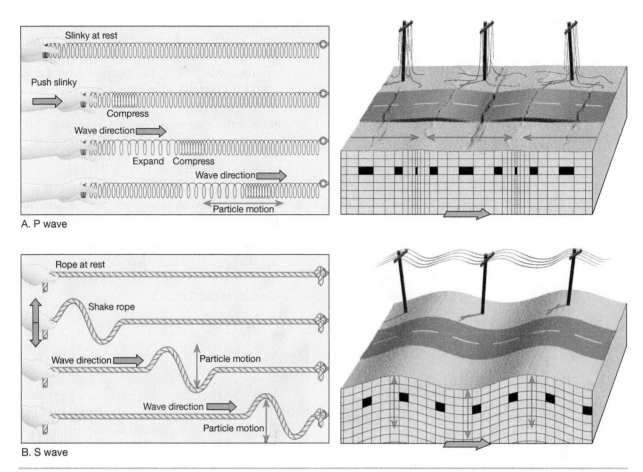

Figure 4 Types of seismic waves and their characteristic motion. (Note that during a strong earthquake, ground shaking consists of a combination of various kinds of seismic waves.) **A.** As illustrated by a slinky, P waves are compressional waves that alternately compress and expand the material through which they pass. The back-and-forth motion produced as compressional waves travel along the surface can cause the ground to buckle and fracture, and may cause power lines to break **B.** S waves cause material to oscillate at right angles to the direction of wave motion. Because S waves can travel in any plane, they produce up-and-down and sideways shaking of the ground.

To determine the distance between a recording station and an earthquake epicenter, find the place on the travel-time graph, Figure 5, where the vertical separation between the P and S curves is equal to the number of minutes difference in the arrival times between the first P and first S waves on the seismogram. From this position, a vertical line is drawn that extends to the top or bottom of the graph and the distance to the epicenter is read.

To accurately locate an earthquake epicenter, records from three different seismograph stations are needed. First, the distance that each station is from the epicenter is determined using Figure 5. Then, for each station, a circle centered on the station with a radius equal to the station's distance from the epicenter is drawn. The geographic point where all three circles, one for each station, intersect is the earthquake epicenter (Figure 6).

Answering questions 7–16 will help you understand the process used to determine an earthquake epicenter.

7. An examination of Figure 5 shows that the difference in the arrival times of the first P and the first S waves on a seismogram (increases, decreases), the farther a station is from the epicenter. Circle your answer.

8. Use Figure 5 to determine the difference in arrival times (in minutes) between the first P wave and first S wave for stations that are the following distances from an epicenter.

1,000 miles: _____ minutes difference

2,400 km: _____ minutes difference

3,000 miles: _____ minutes difference

On the seismogram in Figure 3, you determined the difference in the arrival times between the first P and the first S waves to be five minutes.

9. Refer to the travel-time graph. What is the distance from the epicenter to the station that recorded the earthquake in Figure 3?

_____ miles

51

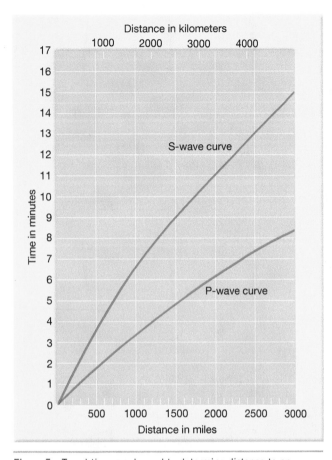

Figure 5 Travel-time graph used to determine distance to an earthquake epicenter.

10. From the travel-time (minutes) axis of the travel-time graph, the first P waves from the seismogram in Figure 3 arrived at the recording station approximately (3, 7, 14) minutes after the earthquake occurred. Circle your answer.

11. If the first P wave was recorded at 10:39 P.M. local time at the station in Figure 3, what was the local time when the earthquake actually occurred?

_____ P.M. local time

Figure 7 illustrates seismograms for the same earthquake recorded at New York, Seattle, and Mexico City. Use this information to answer questions 12–16.

12. Use the travel-time graph, Figure 5, to determine the distance that each station in Figure 7 is from the epicenter. Write your answers in the epicenter data table, Table 1.

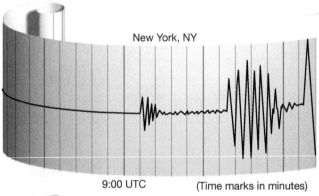

New York, NY

9:00 UTC   (Time marks in minutes)

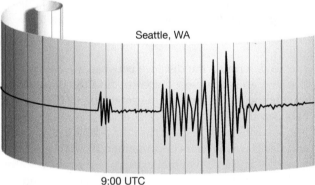

Seattle, WA

9:00 UTC

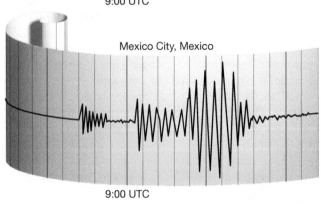

Mexico City, Mexico

9:00 UTC

Figure 6 An earthquake epicenter is located using the distances obtained from three or more seismic stations.

Figure 7 Three seismograms of the same earthquake recorded at three different locations.

Table 1 Epicenter Data Table

	NEW YORK	SEATTLE	MEXICO CITY
Elapsed time between first P and first S waves			
Distance from epicenter in miles			

13. After referring to an atlas or wall map, accurately place a small dot showing the location of each of the three stations on the map provided in Figure 8. Also label each of the three cities.

14. On Figure 8, use a drawing compass to draw a circle around each of the three stations with a radius, in miles, equal to its distance from the epicenter. (*Note:* Use the distance scale provided on the map to set the distance on the drawing compass for each station.)

15. What is the approximate latitude and longitude of the epicenter of the earthquake that was recorded by the three stations?

_____ latitude and _____ longitude

16. Note on the seismograms that the first P wave was recorded in New York at 9:01 Coordinated Universal Time (UTC, the international standard on which most nations base their civil time). At what time (UTC) did the earthquake actually occur?

_____ UTC

Global Distribution of Earthquakes

Earth scientists have determined that the global distribution of earthquakes is not random but follows a few relatively narrow belts that wind around Earth. Figure 9 illustrates the world distribution of earthquakes for a period of several years. Use the figure to answer questions 17 and 18.

17. With what Earth feature is each of the following earthquake belts associated?

Western and southern Pacific Ocean basin: _____

_____

Western South America: _____

_____

Mid-Atlantic Ocean basin: _____

_____

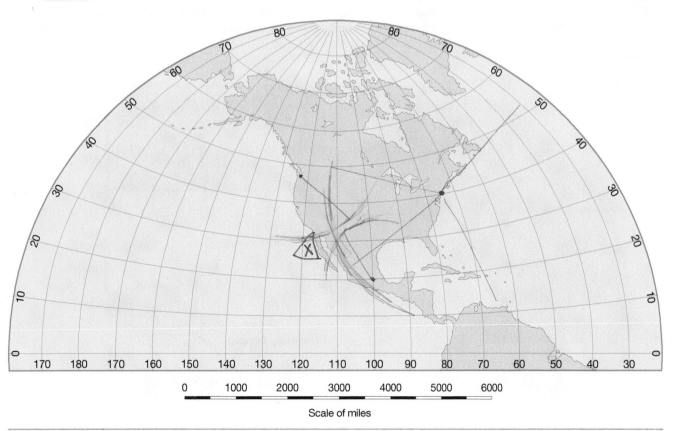

Figure 8 Map for locating an earthquake epicenter.

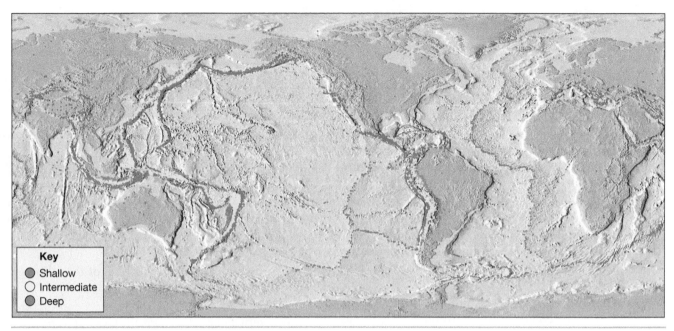

Figure 9 World distribution of shallow-, intermediate-, and deep-focus earthquakes. (Data from NOAA)

18. The belts of earthquake activity follow closely the boundaries of what Earth phenomenon?

_____

The Earth Beyond Our View

The study of earthquakes has contributed greatly to Earth scientists' understanding of the internal structure of Earth. Variations in the travel times of P and S waves as they journey through Earth provide scientists with an indication of changes in rock properties. Also, since S waves cannot travel through fluids, the fact that they are not present in seismic waves that penetrate deep into Earth suggests a fluid zone near Earth's center.

In addition to the lithosphere, the other major zones of Earth's interior include the **asthenosphere**, **mantle**, **outer core**, and **inner core**. After you have reviewed these zones and the general structure of the Earth's interior, use Figure 10 to answer questions 19–24.

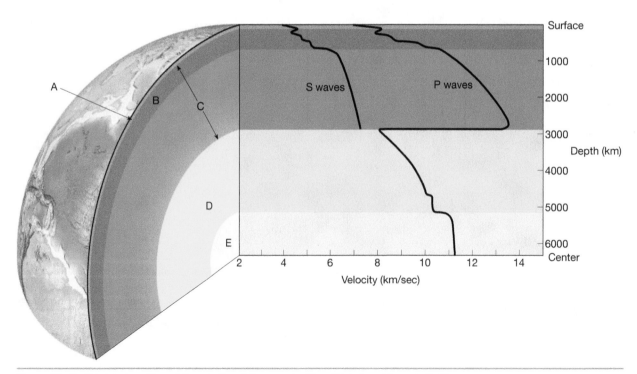

Figure 10 Earth's interior with variations in P and S wave velocities. (Data from Bruce A. Bolt)

19. The layer labeled A on Figure 10 is the solid, rigid, upper zone of Earth that extends from the surface to a depth of about (100, 500, 1,000) kilometers. Circle your answer.

    a. Zone A is called the (core, mantle, lithosphere).

    b. What are the approximate velocities of P and S waves in zone A?

    P wave velocity: _____ km/sec

    S wave velocity: _____ km/sec

    c. The velocity of both P and S waves (increases, decreases) with increased depth in zone A. Circle your answer.

    d. List the two parts of Earth's *crust* that are included in zone A and briefly describe the composition of each.

    1) _____: _____

    _____

    2) _____: _____

    _____

20. Zone B is the part of Earth's upper mantle that extends from the base of zone A to a depth of up to about (180, 660, 2,250) kilometers in some regions of Earth. Circle your answer.

    a. Zone B is called the (crust, asthenosphere, core).

    b. The velocity of P and S waves (increases, decreases) immediately below zone A in the upper part of zone B.

    c. The change in velocity of the S waves in zone B indicates that it (is, is not) similar to zone A.

21. Zone C (which includes the lower part of zone A and zone B) extends to a depth of

    _____ kilometers.

    a. Zone C is called Earth's _____.

    b. What fact concerning S waves indicates that zone C is not liquid?

    _____

    _____

    c. What is the probable composition of zone C?

    _____

22. Zone D extends from 2,885 km to about (5,100, 6,100) kilometers.

    a. Zone D is Earth's _____ _____.

    b. What happens to S waves when they reach zone D, and what does this indicate about the zone?

    _____

    _____

    _____

    _____

    c. The velocity of P waves (increases, decreases) as they enter zone D. Circle your answer.

23. Zone E is Earth's _____ _____.

    a. Zone E extends from a depth of _____ km to the _____ of Earth.

    b. What change in velocity do P waves exhibit at the top of zone E, and what does this suggest about the zone?

    _____

    _____

    _____

    _____

    c. What is the probable composition of Earth's core?

    _____

    _____

24. Label Figure 10 by writing the name of each interior zone at the appropriate letter.

Earth's Internal Temperature

Measurements of temperatures in wells and mines have shown that Earth's temperatures increase with depth. The rate of temperature increase is called the **geothermal gradient.** Although the geothermal gradient varies from place to place, it is possible to calculate an average. Table 2 shows an idealized average temperature gradient for the upper Earth compiled from many different sources. Use the information in Table 2 to answer questions 25–29.

Table 2 Idealized Internal Temperatures of Earth Compiled from Several Sources

DEPTH (KILOMETERS)	TEMPERATURE (°C)
0	20°
25	600°
50	1000°
75	1250°
100	1400°
150	1700°
200	1800°

Table 3 Melting Temperatures of Granite (with water) and Basalt at Various Depths within Earth

GRANITE (WITH WATER)		BASALT	
DEPTH (KM)	MELTING TEMP. (°C)	DEPTH (KM)	MELTING TEMP. (°C)
0	950°	0	1100°
5	700°	25	1160°
10	660°	50	1250°
20	625°	100	1400°
40	600°	150	1600°

25. Plot the temperature values from Table 2 on the graph in Figure 11. Then draw a single line that fits the pattern of points from the surface to 200 km. Label the line "temperature gradient."

26. Refer to the graph in Figure 11. The rate of increase of Earth's internal temperature (is constant, changes) with increasing depth. Circle your answer.

27. The rate of temperature increase from the surface to 100 km is (greater, less) than the rate of increase below 100 km.

28. The temperature at the base of the lithosphere, which is about 100 kilometers below the surface, is approximately (600, 1,400, 1,800) degrees Celsius.

29. Use the data and graph to calculate the average temperature gradient (temperature change per unit of depth) for the upper 100 km of Earth in °C/100 km and °C/km.

°C/100 km: _____, °C/km: _____

Melting Temperatures of Rocks

Geologists have always been concerned with the conditions required for pockets of molten rock (magma) to form near the surface, as well as at what depth within

Earth a general melting of rock may occur. The melting temperature of a rock changes as pressure increases deeper within Earth. The approximate melting points of the igneous rocks, granite and basalt, under various pressures (depths) have been determined in the laboratory and are shown in Table 3. Granite and basalt have been selected because they are the common materials of the upper Earth. Use the data in Table 3 to answer questions 30–35.

30. Plot the melting temperature data from Table 3 on the Earth's internal temperature graph you have prepared in Figure 11. Draw a different colored line for each set of points and label them "melting curve for wet granite" and "melting curve for basalt."

Use the graphs you have drawn in Figure 11 to help answer questions 31–33.

31. Assume your Earth temperature gradient is accurate. At approximately what depth within Earth would wet granite reach its melting temperature and form granitic magma?

_____ km within Earth

32. Evidence suggests that the oceanic crust and the remaining lithosphere down to a depth of about 100 km are similar in composition to basalt. The melting curve for basalt indicates that the lithosphere above approximately 100 km (has, has not) reached the melting temperature for basalt and therefore should be (solid, molten). Circle your answers.

33. Figure 11 indicates that basalt reaches its melting temperature within Earth at a depth of approximately _____ km. (Solid, Partly melted) basaltic material would be expected to occur below this depth. Circle your answer.

34. Referring to Figure 10, what is the name of the zone within Earth that begins at a depth of about 100 km and may extend to approximately 700 km?

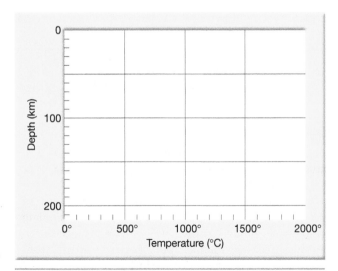

Figure 11 Graph for plotting temperature curves.

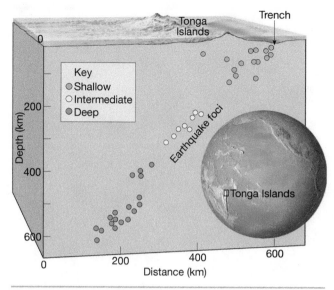

Figure 12 Distribution of earthquake foci in 1965 in the vicinity of the Tonga Islands. (Data from B. Isacks, J. Oliver, and L. R. Sykes)

35. Why do scientists believe that the zone in question 34 is capable of "flowing"?

_____

_____

Earthquakes and Earth Temperatures—A Practical Application

The study of earthquakes and Earth's internal temperature has contributed greatly to the understanding of plate tectonics. One part of the plate tectonics theory is that large, rigid slabs of the lithosphere are descending into the mantle where they generate deep focus earthquakes. Using earthquakes and Earth temperatures, Earth scientists have confirmed that this major Earth process is currently taking place near the Tonga Islands in the South Pacific and elsewhere.

Figure 12 illustrates the distribution of earthquake foci during a one-year period in the vicinity of the Tonga Islands. Use the figure to answer questions 36–40.

36. At approximately what depth do the deepest earthquakes occur in the area represented on Figure 12?

_____ kilometers

37. The earthquake foci in the area are distributed (in a random manner, nearly along a line). Circle your answer.

38. On the figure, outline the area of earthquakes within Earth.

39. Using previous information from this exercise, draw a line on Figure 12 at the proper depth that indicates the top of the *asthenosphere*—the zone of partly melted or plastic Earth material. Label the line "top of asthenosphere."

40. Recall the cause and mechanism of earthquakes. Why have Earth scientists been drawn to the conclusion of a descending slab of solid lithosphere being consumed into the mantle near Tonga?

_____

_____

_____

_____

Earthquakes on the Internet

Continue your exploration of earthquakes by completing the corresponding online activity on the *Applications & Investigations in Earth Science* website at http://prenhall.com/earthsciencelab

Notes and calculations.

Earthquakes and Earth's Interior

Date Due: _____

Name: _____

Date: _____

Class: _____

After you have finished this exercise, complete the following questions. You may have to refer to the exercise for assistance or to locate specific answers. Be prepared to submit this summary/report to your instructor at the designated time.

1. Use the minute marks provided below to sketch a typical seismogram where the first P wave arrives three minutes ahead of the first S wave. Label each type of wave.

. . . .

(minute marks)

2. How far from the earthquake epicenter is the seismic station that recorded the seismogram in question 1 of this Summary/Report page?

_____ miles

3. Use a diagram to explain how the epicenter of an earthquake is located.

Explanation: _____

_____

_____

_____

_____

_____

_____

Epicenter Diagram

4. What are three Earth features associated with earthquakes?

_____

_____

5. The change in velocity of S waves at the top of the asthenosphere suggests that it is (similar to, different from) the lithosphere. Circle your answer.

6. Why don't S waves make it through Earth's outer core?

_____

_____

_____

59

7. List the depths of the following interior zones of Earth.

Crust: depth (km) from _____ to _____

Mantle: depth (km) from _____ to _____

Outer core: depth (km) from _____ to _____

Inner core: depth (km) from _____ to _____

8. On the internal temperature graph you constructed in Figure 11, at what depth did you determine granitic magma should form?

_____ kilometers

9. Why do Earth scientists think that rigid slabs of the lithosphere are descending into the mantle near the Tonga Islands?

_____

_____

10. Define the following terms:

Earthquake focus: _____

_____

Earthquake epicenter: _____

_____

Seismogram: _____

_____

Asthenosphere: _____

_____

Geothermal gradient: _____

_____

Lithosphere: _____

_____

11. Identify, label, and describe each of Earth's interior zones on Figure 13.

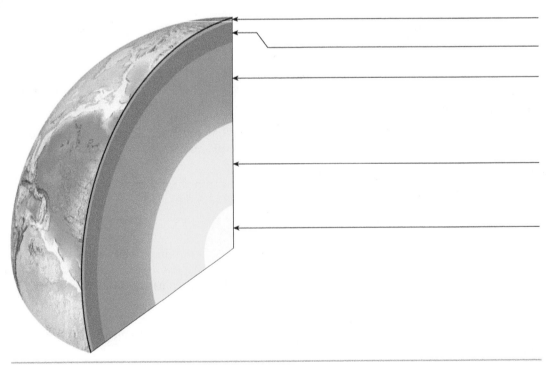

Figure 13 Earth's interior zones.

Air Masses, the Middle-Latitude Cyclone, and Weather Maps

For many people living in the middle latitudes, weather patterns are the result of the movements of large bodies of air and the associated interactions among the weather elements. Of particular importance are the boundaries between contrasting bodies of air, which are often associated with precipitation followed by a change in weather.

This exercise investigates those atmospheric phenomena that most often influence our day-to-day weather—air masses, fronts, and traveling middle-latitude cyclones. Using the standard techniques for plotting weather station data, the exercise concludes with the preparation and analysis of a typical December surface weather map.

Objectives

After you have completed this exercise, you should be able to:

1. Discuss the characteristics, movements, and source regions of North American air masses.
2. Define and draw a profile of a typical warm front.
3. Define and draw a profile of a typical cold front.
4. Diagram and label all parts of an idealized, mature, middle-latitude cyclone.
5. Interpret the data presented on a surface weather map.
6. Prepare a simple surface weather map using standard techniques.
7. Use a surface weather map to forecast the weather for a city.

Materials

colored pencils

Materials Supplied by Your Instructor

United States map or atlas

Terms

air mass	occluded front	anticyclone
source region	adiabatic cooling	middle-latitude
front	polar front	cyclone
warm front	instability	wave cyclones
cold front		

Air Masses

An **air mass** is a large body of air that has relatively uniform temperature and moisture characteristics. The area where an air mass acquires its traits is called a **source region**. For example, air with a source region over cool ocean water tends to become cool and moist, while air that stagnates over the American Southwest in summer becomes hot and dry.

Air masses are set into motion by passing high and low pressure cells. When the air mass moves out of its source region, its temperature and moisture conditions are carried with it.

1. Air masses are classified according to their source region: land versus water and latitude of origin. Explain the meaning of each of the following air mass classification letters.

   c: _____   P: _____

   m: _____   T: _____

Figure 1 shows the source regions and directions of movement of the air masses that play an important role in the weather of North America. Use the figure to answer questions 2–8.

Figure 1 Source regions of North American air masses.

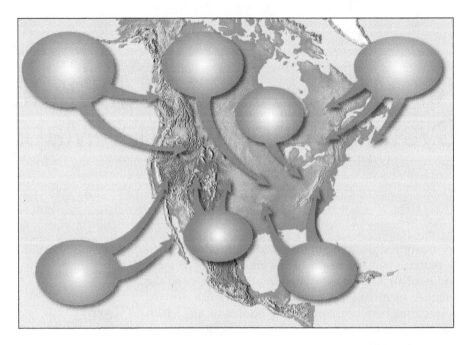

2. Label each of the following North American air masses on Figure 1. Then list the location of the source region of each in the following space.

SOURCE REGION

cP: _____

cT: _____

mP: _____

mT: _____

3. What would be the typical winter temperature and moisture characteristics of each of the following air masses?

	TEMPERATURE	MOISTURE
cP:	_____	_____
mP:	_____	_____
mT:	_____	_____

Notice the paths of air masses indicated by the arrows on Figure 1.

4. The general movement of air masses across North America is (east to west, west to east). Circle your answer.

5. How does the movement of air masses across North America correspond to the global flow of wind over the continent?

_____

6. Which air masses would have the greatest influence on the weather east of the Rocky Mountains?

_____

7. A (cP, mT) air mass would supply the greatest amount of moisture east of the Rocky Mountains. Circle your answer.

8. A (cP, mP) air mass has the greatest influence on the weather along the northwest Pacific coast. Circle your answer.

Fronts

A **front** is a surface of contact between air masses of different densities. One air mass is often warmer, less dense, and higher in moisture content than the other. There is little mixing of air across a front, and each air mass retains its basic characteristics. A **warm front**, shown on a weather map by the symbol ⬤⬤⬤⬤, occurs where warm air occupies an area formerly covered by cooler air. A **cold front**, indicated on a map with the symbol ▲▲▲▲, forms when cold air actively advances into a region occupied by warmer air. An **occluded front**, shown on a weather map with the symbol ⬤▲⬤▲, develops when a cold front overtakes a warm front and warm air is wedged above cold surface air.

Fronts typically act as barriers or walls over which air must rise. When it rises, air will expand and experience **adiabatic cooling**. As a consequence, clouds and precipitation often occur along fronts.

9. On Figure 1, draw a line where air masses are likely to collide and fronts develop. Where does this boundary occur?

_____

10. In the central United States, east of the Rocky Mountains, a (cP, mT) air mass will most likely be

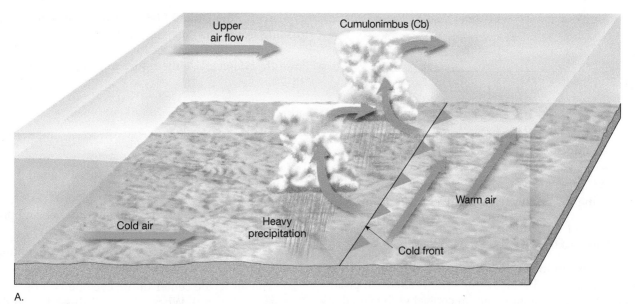

A.

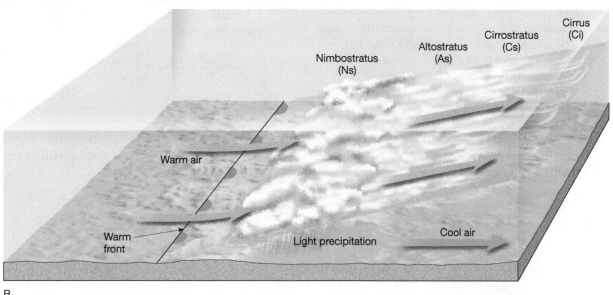

B.

Figure 2   **A.** Typical cold front profile. **B.** Typical warm-front profile.

found north of a front, and a (cP, mT) mass to the south. Circle your answers.

Figure 2 illustrates profiles through typical cold and warm fronts. Observe the profiles closely and then answer questions 11–17.

11. Along the (cold, warm) front, the cold air is the aggressive or "pushing" air. Circle your answer.

12. Along the (cold, warm) front, the warm air rises at the steepest angle.

13. Along which front are extensive areas of stratus clouds and periods of prolonged precipitation most probable? Explain why you expect longer

periods of precipitation to be associated with this type of front.

_____ front. Explanation:_____

_____

14. Assume that the fronts are moving from left to right in Figure 2. A drop in temperature is most likely to occur with the passing of a (cold, warm) front. Circle your answer.

The air following a cold front is frequently cold, dense, and subsiding.

15. (Clear, Cloudy) conditions are most likely to pre-vail after a cold front passes. Explain the reason

for your choice with reference to the adiabatic process.

_____

_____

16. Clouds of vertical development and perhaps thunderstorms are most likely to occur along a (cold, warm) front.

17. As a (cold, warm) front approaches, clouds become lower, thicker, and cover more of the sky.

Middle-Latitude Cyclone

Contrasting air masses frequently collide in the area of the *subpolar lows*. In this region, often called the **polar front**, warm, moist air comes in contact with cool, dry air in an area of low pressure. These conditions present an ideal situation for atmospheric **instability**, rising air, adiabatic cooling, condensation, and precipitation. In contrast, in areas of high pressure, called **anticyclones**, the air typically is subsiding.

In the Northern Hemisphere, the westerly winds to the south of the polar front and the easterly winds to the north cause a wave with counterclockwise (cyclonic) rotation to form along the frontal surface. As the low-pressure system called a **middle-latitude** (or **wave**) **cyclone** evolves, it follows a general eastward path across the United States, bringing a sequence of passing fronts and changing weather.

Figure 3 illustrates an idealized, mature, middle-latitude cyclone. Use the figure to complete questions 18–28.

18. On Figure 3:

  a. Label the cold front, warm front, and occluded front.

  b. Draw arrows showing the surface wind directions at points A, C, E, F, and G.

  c. Label the sectors most likely experiencing precipitation with the word "precipitation."

19. The surface winds in the cyclone are (converging, diverging). Circle your answer.

20. The air in the center of the cyclone will be (subsiding, rising). What effect will this have on the potential for condensation and precipitation? Explain your answer.

_____

_____

21. As the middle-latitude cyclone moves eastward, the barometric pressure at point A will be (rising, falling). Circle your answer.

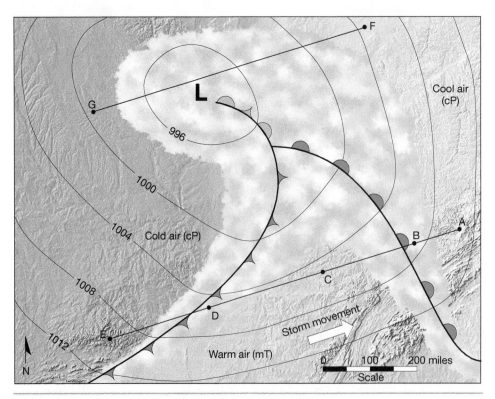

Figure 3 Mature, middle-latitude cyclone (idealized).

22. After the warm front passes, the wind at point B will be from the (south, north).

23. Describe the changes in wind direction and barometric pressure that will likely occur at point D after the cold front passes.

_____

_____

24. Considering the typical air mass types and their locations in a middle-latitude cyclone, the amount of water vapor in the air will most likely (increase, decrease) at A after the warm front passes.

25. The quantity of moisture in the air at point D will most likely (increase, decrease) after the cold front passes.

26. Use Figure 3 to describe the sequence of weather conditions—barometric changes, wind directions, humidity, precipitation, etc.—expected for a city as the cyclone moves and the city's relative position changes from location A to B, and then to C, D, and E.

_____

_____

_____

_____

27. Near the center of the low, a/an (warm, cold, occluded) front has formed where the cold front has overtaken the warm front. Circle your answer. Then answer questions 27a and 27b.

   a. What happens to the warm mT air in this type of front?

   _____

   b. With reference to the adiabatic process, why is there a good chance for precipitation with this type of front?

   _____

   _____

After the entire wave cyclone passes, pressure will rise.

28. Describe the general weather often associated with a high pressure cell, called an anticyclone.

_____

_____

As mentioned previously, middle-latitude cyclones form in the belt of subpolar lows. After you have reviewed the subpolar lows in Exercise 14, answer the following question by circling the correct responses.

29. During the (summer, winter) season the belt of subpolar lows and the polar front are farthest south in North America, and the central United States will experience a (greater, lesser) frequency of passing middle-latitude cyclones.

Weather Station Analysis and Forecasting

In order to understand, analyze, and predict the weather, observers at hundreds of weather stations throughout the United States collect and record weather data several times a day. This information is forwarded to offices of the National Weather Service where it and satellite data are computer processed and mapped. Weather maps, containing data from throughout the country, are then distributed to any interested individual or agency.

Weather Station Data

To manage the great quantity of information necessary for accurate maps, meteorologists have developed a system for coding weather data. Figure 4 illustrates the system and many of the symbols that are used to record data for a weather station. (*Note:* When plotting barometric pressure in millibars for a weather station, to conserve space, the initial number 9 or 10 is omitted and the last digit is tenths of a millibar. For example, on a map a barometric pressure of 216 for a station would be read as 1021.6 mb.)

Figure 5 is a coded weather station, shown as it would appear on a simplified surface weather map.

30. Using the specimen station model and explanations shown in Figure 4 as your guide, interpret the weather conditions reported at the station illustrated in Figure 5.

   Percent of sky cover: _____ %

   Wind direction: _____

   Wind speed: _____ mph

   Temperature: _____ °F

   Dew-point temperature: _____ °F

   Barometric pressure: _____ millibars

   Barometric change in past 3 hours: _____ mb

   Weather during the past 6 hours: _____

31. Encode and plot the weather conditions for the following weather station on the station symbol

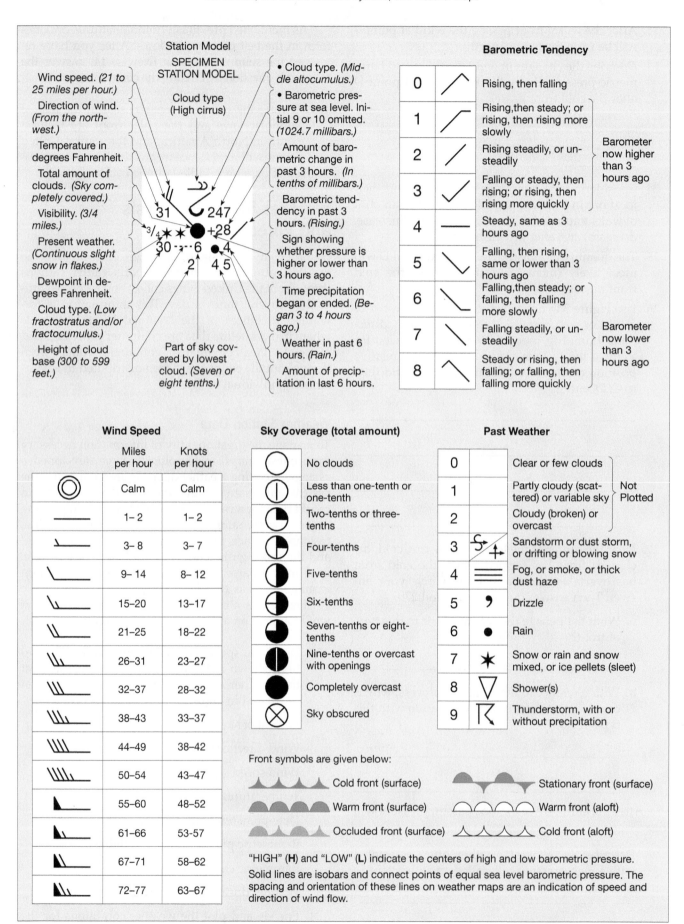

Station Model

SPECIMEN STATION MODEL

Wind speed. *(21 to 25 miles per hour.)*

Direction of wind. *(From the northwest.)*

Temperature in degrees Fahrenheit.

Total amount of clouds. *(Sky completely covered.)*

Visibility. *(3/4 miles.)*

Present weather. *(Continuous slight snow in flakes.)*

Dewpoint in degrees Fahrenheit.

Cloud type. *(Low fractostratus and/or fractocumulus.)*

Height of cloud base *(300 to 599 feet.)*

Cloud type (High cirrus)

• Cloud type. *(Middle altocumulus.)*

• Barometric pressure at sea level. Initial 9 or 10 omitted. *(1024.7 millibars.)*

Amount of barometric change in past 3 hours. *(In tenths of millibars.)*

Barometric tendency in past 3 hours. *(Rising.)*

Sign showing whether pressure is higher or lower than 3 hours ago.

Time precipitation began or ended. *(Began 3 to 4 hours ago.)*

Weather in past 6 hours. *(Rain.)*

Amount of precipitation in last 6 hours.

Part of sky covered by lowest cloud. *(Seven or eight tenths.)*

Barometric Tendency

0	/\	Rising, then falling
1	/	Rising, then steady; or rising, then rising more slowly
2	/	Rising steadily, or unsteadily
3	✓	Falling or steady, then rising; or rising, then rising more quickly
4	—	Steady, same as 3 hours ago
5	\	Falling, then rising, same or lower than 3 hours ago
6	\	Falling, then steady; or falling, then falling more slowly
7	\	Falling steadily, or unsteadily
8	\/	Steady or rising, then falling; or falling, then falling more quickly

Barometer now higher than 3 hours ago

Barometer now lower than 3 hours ago

Wind Speed

	Miles per hour	Knots per hour
◎	Calm	Calm
—	1–2	1–2
\\	3–8	3–7
\\	9–14	8–12
\\	15–20	13–17
\\	21–25	18–22
\\	26–31	23–27
\\	32–37	28–32
\\	38–43	33–37
\\	44–49	38–42
\\	50–54	43–47
\\	55–60	48–52
\\	61–66	53–57
\\	67–71	58–62
\\	72–77	63–67

Sky Coverage (total amount)

○	No clouds
◐	Less than one-tenth or one-tenth
◔	Two-tenths or three-tenths
◑	Four-tenths
◑	Five-tenths
◕	Six-tenths
◕	Seven-tenths or eight-tenths
◕	Nine-tenths or overcast with openings
●	Completely overcast
⊗	Sky obscured

Past Weather

0		Clear or few clouds
1		Partly cloudy (scattered) or variable sky
2		Cloudy (broken) or overcast
3		Sandstorm or dust storm, or drifting or blowing snow
4	≡	Fog, or smoke, or thick dust haze
5	,	Drizzle
6	•	Rain
7	✳	Snow or rain and snow mixed, or ice pellets (sleet)
8	▽	Shower(s)
9	⍐	Thunderstorm, with or without precipitation

Not Plotted

Front symbols are given below:

▲▲▲ Cold front (surface)

⌒⌒⌒ Warm front (surface)

▲⌒▲ Occluded front (surface)

⌒▲⌒ Stationary front (surface)

⌒⌒⌒ Warm front (aloft)

△△△ Cold front (aloft)

"HIGH" (**H**) and "LOW" (**L**) indicate the centers of high and low barometric pressure.

Solid lines are isobars and connect points of equal sea level barometric pressure. The spacing and orientation of these lines on weather maps are an indication of speed and direction of wind flow.

Figure 4   Specimen weather station model and standard symbols. (Source: Daily Weather Maps, U.S. Department of Commerce)

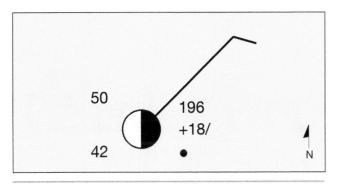

Figure 5 Coded weather station (abbreviated).

(992 mb, 996 mb, 1,000 mb, etc.). (*Note:* You will have to estimate pressures between cities to determine the location of isobars. Also, it may be a good idea to first sketch the isobars lightly in pencil.)

Step 2: By observing the data plotted on the map, determine the locations of the cold and warm fronts. Using the proper symbols, label the cold and warm fronts as accurately as possible on the map.

Step 3: Label the air mass types that are most likely to be located to the northwest and to the southeast of the cold front.

Step 4: Indicate areas of precipitation by lightly shading the map with a pencil.

shown below. Use Figures 4 and 5 as your guides.

The sky is six-tenths covered by clouds. Air temperature is 82°F with a dew point of 50°F. Wind is from the south at 22 miles per hour. Barometric pressure is 1022.4 millibars and has fallen from 1023.0 millibars during the past three hours. There has been no precipitation during the past six hours.

33. Assume that the middle-latitude cyclone illustrated on the map was centered in Oklahoma the previous day and is moving northeastward. Indicate your forecast (temperature, wind direction, probability of precipitation, cloud cover, and barometric pressure) for the next 12–24 hours at the following locations.

Chattanooga, TN: _____

_____

_____

Little Rock, AR: _____

_____

_____

Washington, D.C.: _____

_____

_____

Raleigh, NC: _____

_____

_____

Preparing a Weather Map and Forecast

Table 1 contains weather data for several cities in the central and eastern United States on a December day. Data for several of the cities have been plotted on the map, Figure 6. Use Table 1 and Figure 6 to complete questions 32 and 33.

32. Refer to stations where the data have already been plotted and the station model in Figure 4. Plot the data for the remaining stations on the map. Then complete the following steps.

Step 1: Beginning with 988 millibars, draw isobars as accurately as possible at four millibar intervals

Weather Maps on the Internet

Apply the concepts from this exercise to an analysis of the current weather patterns in North America by completing the corresponding online activity on the *Applications & Investigations in Earth Science* website at http://prenhall.com/earthsciencelab

Table 1 December Surface Weather Data for Selected Cities in the Central and Eastern United States

STATION	% CLOUD COVER	WIND DIRECTION	WIND SPEED (MPH)	TEMP.	DEW PT. TEMP.	PRESSURE (MB)	PRESSURE 3 HOUR + OR −	PRECIP.
Atlanta, GA	20	SE	18	61	56	1000.7	−2.0	
Birmingham, AL	80	SW	15	70	64	998.1	−1.4	
Charleston, SC	10	SE	12	63	58	1008.0	−2.0	
Charlotte, NC	70	SW	14	54	49	1003.4	−4.4	Drizzle
Chattanooga, TN	60	SW	12	66	60	995.3	−2.5	Drizzle
Chicago, IL	100	NE	13	34	21	1003.2	−2.2	
Columbus, OH	100	E	10	34	28	996.8	−5.8	Snow
Evansville, IN	100	NW	7	45	43	987.2	−2.7	Snow
Fort Worth, TX	0	NW	5	46	43	1002.6	+1.4	
Indianapolis, IN	100	NE	30	34	32	993.2	−5.6	Snow
Jackson, MS	40	SW	10	72	67	1001.3	+1.2	Thunderstorm
Kansas City, MO	30	N	18	30	27	1005.5	+1.7	
Little Rock, AR	0	NW	10	46	43	1001.5	+2.7	
Louisville, KY	100	E	12	34	34	993.0	−4.2	Snow
Memphis, TN	80	NW	12	50	45	996.7	+5.8	
Mobile, AL	60	SW	10	72	68	1004.3	−0.3	
Nashville, TN	100	SW	18	56	55	991.5	−0.1	Rain
New Orleans, LA	20	SW	11	75	70	1003.9	−0.1	
New York, NY	100	NE	23	36	18	1016.9	−2.1	
North Platte, NB	30	N	9	9	1	1017.4	+3.2	
Oklahoma City, OK	10	NW	13	41	37	1005.9	+1.5	
Richmond, VA	100	E	10	45	45	1010.9	−2.4	Rain
Roanoke, VA	100	SE	10	39	39	1007.5	−3.6	Snow
Savannah, GA	30	SE	7	61	55	1007.6	−2.0	
Shreveport, LA	0	NW	8	46	43	1002.6	+1.4	
St. Louis, MO	100	NW	10	32	32	999.7	+1.7	Showers
Tampa, FL	50	SE	8	70	66	1011.0	−0.6	

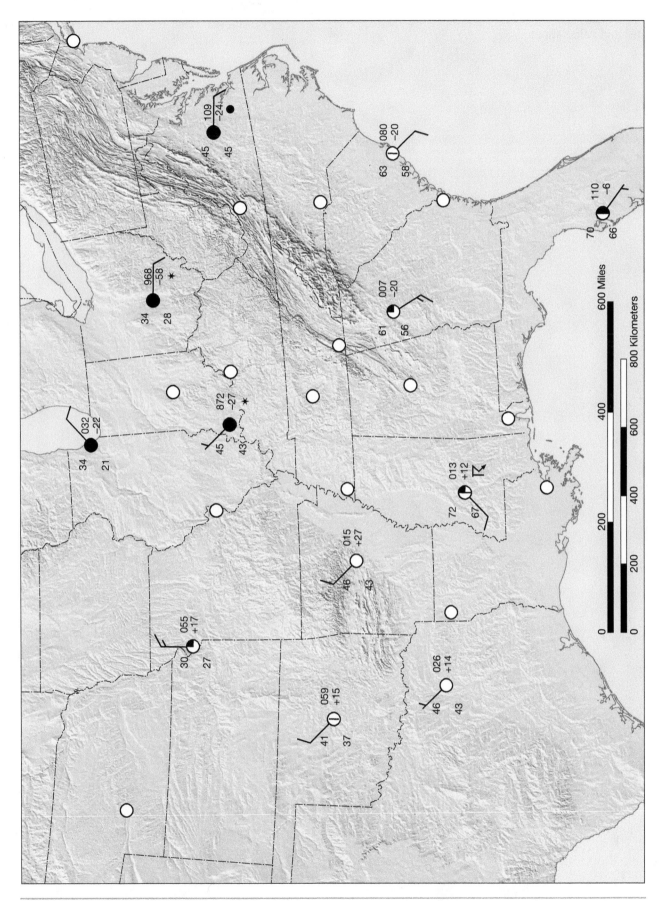

Figure 6 Map of December weather data for selected cities in the central and eastern United States.

Notes and calculations.

Air Masses, the Middle-Latitude Cyclone, and Weather Maps

Date Due: _____

Name: _____

Date: _____

Class: _____

After you have finished this exercise, complete the following questions. You may have to refer to the exercise for assistance or to locate specific answers. Be prepared to submit this summary/report to your instructor at the designated time.

1. List the source region(s) and winter temperature/moisture characteristics of each of the following North American air masses.

   cP: _____

   mT: _____

   mP: _____

2. In the following space, diagram a profile (side view) of an idealized cold front. Label the cold air, warm air, and sketch the probable cloud type at the appropriate location. Draw an arrow on the diagram showing the direction of movement of the front.

   Cold Front Profile

3. Indicate the type of front (cold, warm, or occluded) best described by each of the following statements.

   a. Steep wall of cold air: _____

   b. Warm air replaces cool air: _____

   c. Thunderstorms: _____

   d. Drop in temperature: _____

   e. After passing, wind comes from the south:

   _____

   f. Narrow belt of precipitation: _____

   g. Cold front overtakes warm front: _____

   h. Gradual rise of warm air over cool air: _____

4. Describe the sequence of weather events that a city would experience as an idealized, mature, middle-latitude cyclone that has not developed an occluded front passes over it. Assume that the center of the wave cyclone passes, west to east, 150 miles to the north of the city. Using a diagram may be helpful.

   _____

   _____

   _____

   _____

5. Refer to Figure 7. Draw a sketch of the December weather map that you prepared at the end of the exercise, question 32. Show isobars and wind direction arrows. Indicate and label the fronts.

6. Based on the December weather map that you constructed at the end of the exercise, from question 33, what was your forecast for Little Rock, AR?

_____

_____

7. Write a brief analysis of the weather map in Figure 8.

_____

_____

_____

_____

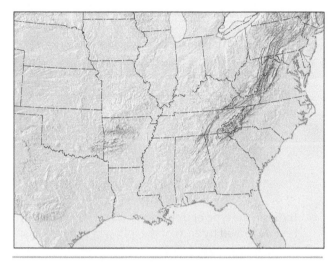

Figure 7 Sketch of the December weather map.

Figure 8 Surface weather map for a March day with a satellite image showing the cloud patterns on that day. (Courtesy of NOAA/Seattle)

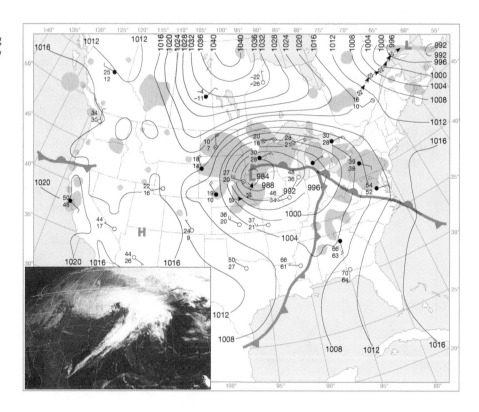

Introduction to Oceanography

The global ocean covers nearly three quarters of Earth's surface and **oceanography** is an important focus of Earth science studies. This exercise investigates some of the physical characteristics of the oceans. To establish a foundation for reference, the extent, depths, and distribution of the world's oceans are the first topics examined. Salinity and temperature, two of the most important variables of seawater, are studied to ascertain how they influence the density of water and the deep ocean circulation (Figure 1).

Objectives

After you have completed this exercise, you should be able to:

1. Locate and name the major water bodies on Earth.

2. Discuss the distribution of land and water in each hemisphere.

3. Locate and describe the general features of ocean basins.

4. Explain the relation between salinity and the density of seawater.

5. Describe how seawater salinity varies with latitude and depth in the oceans.

6. Explain the relation between temperature and the density of seawater.

7. Describe how seawater temperature varies with latitude and depth in the oceans.

Materials

colored pencils · · · · · · · · · · · · · · · ruler

Materials Supplied by Your Instructor

measuring cylinder (100 ml, clear, Pyrex or plastic)	world wall map, globe, or atlas ice	test tubes dye
salt solutions	beaker	salt rubber band

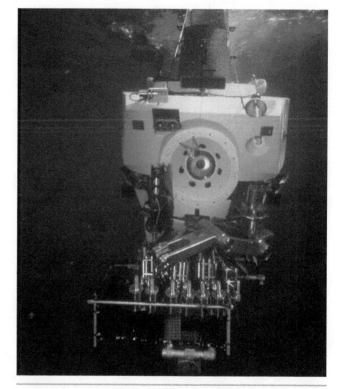

Figure 1 The deep-diving submersible *Alvin* is 7.6 meters long, weighs 16 tons, has a cruising speed of 1 knot, and can reach depths as great as 4000 meters. A pilot and two scientific observers are along during a normal 6- to 10-hour dive. (Courtesy of Rod Catanach/Woods Hole Oceanographic Institution)

Terms

oceanography	deep-ocean trench	submarine
continental shelf	mid-ocean ridge	canyons
continental slope	density	turbidity
abyssal plain	density current	currents
seamount	salinity	

Extent of the Oceans

1. Refer to a globe, wall map of the world, or world map in an atlas and identify each of the oceans

and major water bodies listed below. Locate and label each on the world map, Figure 2.

Oceans	Other Major Water Bodies	
A. Pacific	1. Caribbean Sea	11. Arabian Sea
B. Atlantic	2. North Sea	
C. Indian	3. Coral Sea	12. Weddell Sea
D. Arctic	4. Sea of Japan	
	5. Sea of Okhotsk	13. Bering Sea
	6. Gulf of Mexico	14. Red Sea
	7. Persian Gulf	15. Bay of Bengal
	8. Mediterranean Sea	
	9. Black Sea	16. Caspian Sea
	10. Baltic Sea	

Area

The area of Earth is about 510 million square kilometers (197 million square miles). Of this, approximately 360 million square kilometers (140 million square miles) are covered by oceans and marginal seas.

2. What percentage of Earth's surface is covered by oceans and marginal seas?

$$\frac{\text{Area of oceans and marginal seas}}{\text{Area of Earth}} \times 100$$

= _____ % oceans

3. What percentage of Earth's surface is land?

_____ % land

Distribution of Land and Water by Hemisphere

Answer questions 4–7 by examining either a globe, wall map of the world, world map in an atlas, or Figure 2.

4. a. Which hemisphere, Northern or Southern, could be called the "water" hemisphere and which the "land" hemisphere?

"Water" hemisphere: _____

"Land" hemisphere: _____

b. The oceans become (wider, more narrow) as you go from the equator to the pole in the Northern Hemisphere. Circle your answer.

c. In the Southern Hemisphere the width of the oceans (increases, decreases) from the equator to the pole.

5. Follow a line around a globe, world map, and Figure 3 at the latitudes listed on the following page and estimate what percentage of Earth's surface is ocean at each latitude.

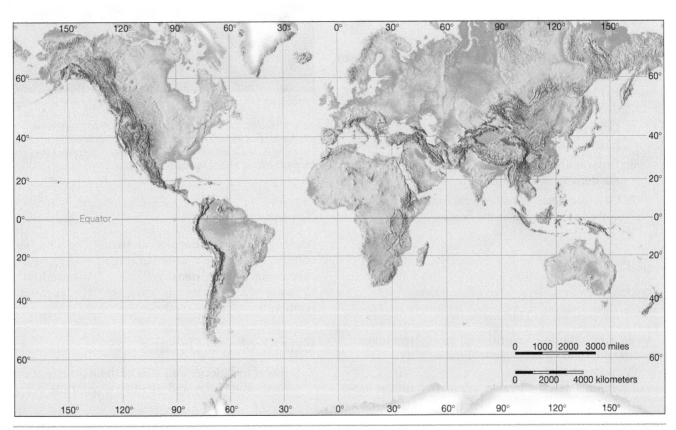

Figure 2 World map.

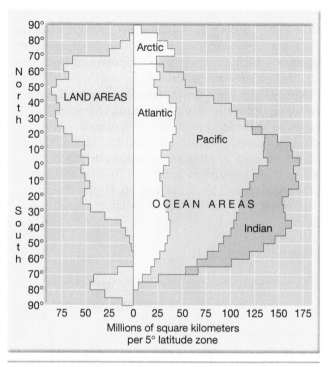

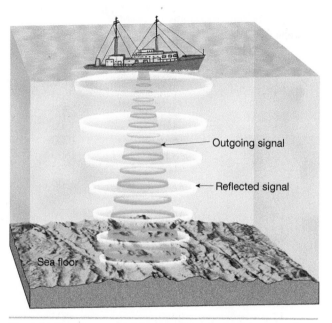

Figure 3 Distribution of land and water in each 5° latitude belt. (After M. Grant Gross, *Oceanography: A View of the Earth*, 2nd ed., Englewood Cliffs, NJ: Prentice-Hall, 1977)

Figure 4 An echo sounder determines the water depth by measuring the time interval required for an acoustic wave to travel from a ship to the seafloor and back. The speed of sound in water is 1,500 m/sec. Therefore, depth = 1/2(1500 m/sec × echo travel time).

	NORTHERN HEMISPHERE	SOUTHERN HEMISPHERE
40°:	_____ % ocean	_____ % ocean
60°:	_____ % ocean	_____ % ocean

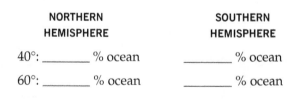

6. Which ocean covers the greatest area?

_____

7. Which ocean is almost entirely in the Southern Hemisphere?

_____

Measuring Ocean Depths

Charting the shape or topography of the ocean floor is a fundamental task of oceanographers. In the 1920s a technological breakthrough for determining ocean depths occurred with the invention of electronic depth-sounding equipment. The **echo sounder** (also referred to as *sonar,* an acronym for *sound navigation and ranging*) works by measuring the precise time that a sound wave, traveling at about 1,500 meters per second in water, takes to reach the ocean floor and return to the instrument (Figure 4). Today, in addition to using sophisticated echo sounders such as *multibeam sonar,* oceanographers are also using satellites to map the ocean floor.

8. Using the formula in Figure 4, calculate the depth of the ocean for each of the following echo soundings.

   5.2 seconds: _____

   6.0 seconds: _____

   2.8 seconds: _____

Ships generally don't make single depth soundings. Rather, as the ship makes a traverse from one location to another, it is continually sending out sound impulses and recording the echoes. In this way, oceanographers obtain many depth recordings from which a *profile* (side view) of the ocean floor can be drawn.

The data in Table 1 were gathered by a ship equipped with an echo sounder as it traveled the North Atlantic Ocean eastward from Cape Cod, Massachusetts. The depths were calculated using the same technique used in question 8.

9. Use the data in Table 1 to construct a generalized profile of the ocean floor in the North Atlantic on Figure 5. Begin by plotting each point at its proper distance from Cape Cod, at the indicated depth. Complete the profile by connecting the depth points.

Table 1 Echo Sounder Depths Eastward from Cape Cod, MA

POINT	DISTANCE (KM)	DEPTH (M)
1	0	0
2	180	200
3	270	2700
4	420	3300
5	600	4000
6	830	4800
7	1100	4750
8	1130	2500
9	1160	4800
10	1490	4750
11	1770	4800
12	1800	500
13	1830	4850
14	2120	4800
15	2320	4000
16	2650	3000
17	2900	1500
18	2950	1000
19	2960	2700
20	3000	2700
21	3050	1000
22	3130	1900

Ocean Basin Topography

Various features are located along the continental margins and on the ocean basin floor (Figure 6). **Continental shelves**, flooded extensions of the continents, are gently sloping submerged surfaces extending from the shoreline toward the ocean basin. The seaward edge of the continental shelf is marked by the **continental slope**, a relatively steep structure (as compared with the shelf) that marks the boundary between continental crust and oceanic crust. Deep, steep-sided valleys known as **submarine canyons**, eroded in part by the periodic downslope movements of dense, sediment-laden water called **turbidity currents**, are often cut into the continental slope. The ocean basin floor, which constitutes almost 30% of Earth's surface, in-

cludes remarkably flat areas known as **abyssal plains**, tall volcanic peaks called **seamounts**, oceanic plateaus generated by mantle plumes, and **deep-ocean trenches**, which are deep linear depressions that occasionally border some continents, primarily in the Pacific Ocean basin. Near the center of most oceanic basins is a topographically elevated feature, characterized by extensive faulting and numerous volcanic structures, called the **oceanic (or mid-ocean) ridge**. Using Figure 6 and a wall map or atlas as references, briefly describe each of these features in questions 10–15. Label one or more examples of each feature on Figure 5 and the ocean floor map of the North Atlantic Ocean basin, Figure 7.

10. Continental shelf: _____

    _____

    a. What is the approximate average ocean depth along the continental shelves bordering North America?

    _____

    b. Write a brief statement comparing the width of the continental shelf along the east coast, west coast, and gulf coast of North America.

    _____

    _____

11. Continental slope: _____

    _____

    a. Briefly describe the origin of submarine canyons and label at least one on Figure 7.

    _____

    _____

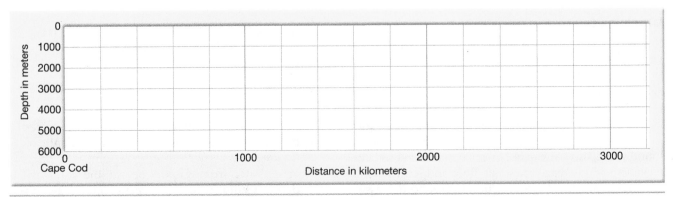

Figure 5 North Atlantic Ocean floor profile (exaggerated).

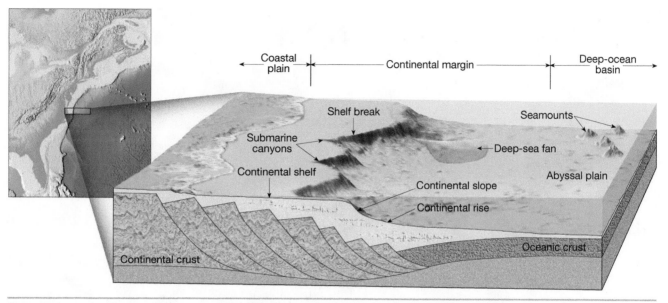

Figure 6 Generalized continental margin. Note that the slopes shown for the continental shelf and continental slope are greatly exaggerated. The continental shelf has an average slope of one tenth of 1 degree, while the continental slope has an average of about 5 degrees.

12. Abyssal plain: _____

_____

a. The general topography of abyssal plains is (flat, irregular). Circle your answer.

b. How do abyssal plains form and what is their composition?

_____

_____

13. Seamount: _____

_____

14. Deep-ocean trench (not shown on Figure 5):

_____

_____

_____

a. Approximately how deep is the Puerto Rico trench?

_____ meters

b. Use a map or globe to locate three deep-ocean trenches in the western Pacific Ocean. Give the name, location, and depth of each.

Trench 1: _____

_____

Trench 2: _____

_____

Trench 3: _____

_____

15. Mid-ocean ridge: _____

_____

a. Examine the mid-ocean ridge system on a world map. Follow the ridge eastward from the Atlantic Ocean into the Indian Ocean and then into the Pacific. Describe what happens to the ridge along the southwest coast of North America.

_____

b. Approximately how high above the adjacent ocean floor does the Mid-Atlantic Ridge rise?

_____ meters

16. Note that Figures 5 and 7 illustrate only the western side of the North Atlantic floor. Using a globe or map, write a brief statement comparing the to-

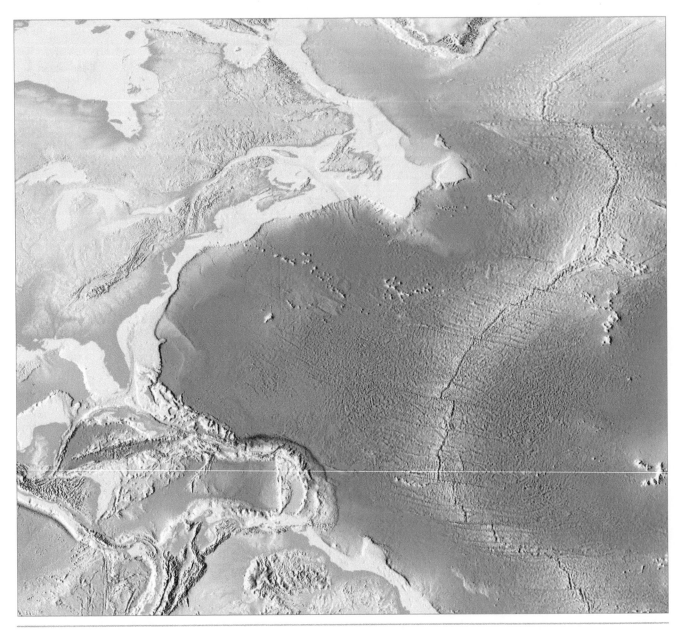

Figure 7   North Atlantic basin.

pography of the North Atlantic Ocean floor east of the mid-ocean ridge to that on the west side.

_____

_____

_____

_____

Characteristics of Ocean Water

Ocean circulation has two primary components: surface ocean currents and deep-ocean circulation. While surface currents like the famous Gulf Stream are driven primarily by the prevailing world winds, the deep-ocean circulation is largely the result of differences in ocean water **density** (mass per unit volume of a substance). A **density current** is the movement (flow) of one body of water over, under, or through another caused by density differences and gravity. Variations in **salinity** and temperature are the two most important factors in creating the density differences that result in the deep-ocean circulation.

Salinity

Salinity is the amount of dissolved solid material in water, expressed as parts per thousand parts of water. The symbol for parts per thousand is 0/00. Although

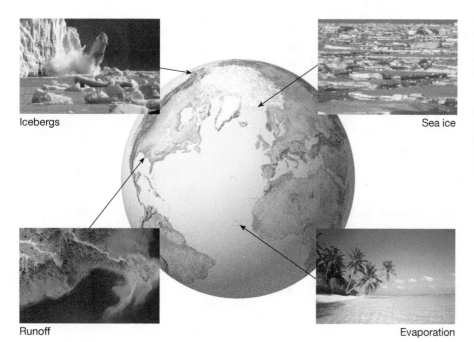

Icebergs

Sea ice

Runoff

Evaporation

Figure 8 Processes affecting seawater salinity. Processes that *decrease* seawater salinity include precipitation, runoff, icebergs melting, and sea ice melting. Processes that *increase* seawater salinity include formation of sea ice and evaporation. Source: (upper left) Tom Bean/Tom and Susan Bean, Inc., (upper right) Wolfgang Kaehler Photography, (lower left) NASA Headquarters, (lower right) Paul Steel/Corbis/Stock Market.

there are many dissolved salts in seawater, sodium chloride (common table salt) is the most abundant.

Variations in the salinity of seawater are primarily a consequence of changes in the water content of the solution. In regions where evaporation is high, the proportionate amount of dissolved material in seawater is increased by removing the water and leaving behind the salts. On the other hand, in areas of high precipitation and high runoff, the additional water dilutes seawater and lowers the salinity. Since the factors that determine the concentration of salts in seawater are not constant from the equator to the poles, the salinity of seawater also varies with latitude and depth (Figure 8).

Salinity–Density Experiment

To gain a better understanding of how salinity affects the density of water, examine the equipment in the lab (see Figure 9) and conduct the following experiment by completing each of the indicated steps.

Step 1. Fill the measuring cylinder with cool tap water up to the rubber band or other marker near the top of the cylinder.

Step 2. Fill a test tube about half full of solution A (saltwater) and pour it slowly into the cylinder. Observe and describe what happens.

Observations: _____

_____

Step 3. Repeat steps 1 and 2 two additional times and measure the time required for the front edge of the saltwater to travel from the rubber band to the bottom of the cylinder. Record the times

for each test in the data table, Table 2. *Make certain* that you drain the cylinder after each trial and refill it with fresh water and use the same amount of solution with each trial.

Step 4. Determine the travel time two times for solution B exactly as you did with solution A and enter your measurements in Table 2.

Figure 9 Lab setup for salinity–density experiment.

Table 2   Salinity–Density Experiment Data Table

SOLUTION	TIMED TRIAL #1	TIMED TRIAL #2	AVERAGE OF BOTH TRIALS
A			
B			
Solution B plus salt		XXXX	XXXX

Step 5. Fill a test tube about half full of solution B and add to it some additional salt. Then shake the test tube vigorously. Determine the travel time of this solution and enter your results in Table 2.

Step 6. Clean all your glassware.

17. Questions 17a and 17b refer to the salinity–density experiment.

   a. Write a brief summary of the results of your salinity–density experiment.

   _____

   _____

   b. Since the solution that traveled fastest has the greatest density, solution (A, B) is most dense. Circle your answer.

Table 3 lists the approximate surface water salinity at various latitudes in the Atlantic and Pacific Oceans. Using the data, construct a salinity curve for each ocean on the graph, Figure 10. *Use a different-colored pencil for each ocean.* Then answer questions 18–22.

Table 3   Ocean Surface Water Salinity in Parts per Thousand (0/00) at Various Latitudes in the Atlantic and Pacific Oceans

LATITUDE	ATLANTIC OCEAN	PACIFIC OCEAN
60°N	33.0 0/00	31.0 0/00
50°	33.7	32.5
40°	34.8	33.2
30°	36.7	34.2
20°	36.8	34.2
10°	36.0	34.4
0°	35.0	34.3
10°	35.9	35.2
20°	36.7	35.6
30°	36.2	35.7
40°	35.3	35.0
50°	34.3	34.4
60°S	33.9	34.0

18. At which latitudes are the highest surface salinities located?

   _____

19. What are two factors that control the concentration of salts in seawater?

   _____ and _____

20. Refer to the factors listed in question 19. What is the cause of the difference in surface water salinity between equatorial and subtropical regions in the Atlantic Ocean?

   _____

   _____

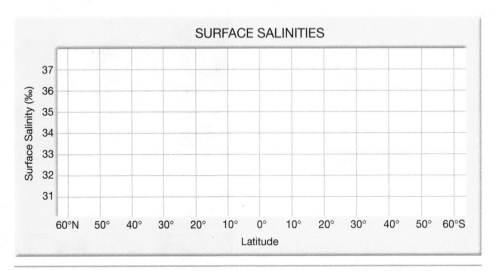

Figure 10 Graph for plotting surface salinities.

80

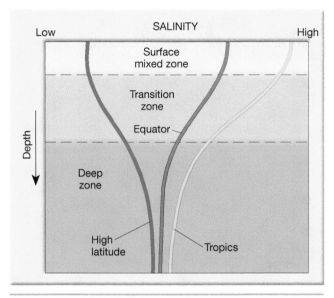

Figure 11 Ocean water salinity changes with depth at high latitudes, equatorial regions, and the tropics.

Ocean Water Temperatures

Seawater temperature is the most extensively determined variable of the oceans because it is easily measured and has an important influence on marine life. Like salinity, ocean water temperatures vary from the equator to poles and also changes with depth.

Temperature, like salinity, also affects the density of seawater. However, the density of seawater is more sensitive to temperature fluctuations than salinity.

Temperature–Density Experiment

To illustrate the effects of temperature on the density of water, examine the equipment in the lab (see Figure 12) and then conduct the following experiment by completing each of the indicated steps.

Step 1. Fill a measuring cylinder with *cold* tap water up to the rubber band.

Step 2. Put 2–3 drops of dye in a test tube and fill it half full with *hot* tap water.

Step 3. Pour the contents of the test tube *slowly* into the cylinder and then record your observations.

Observations: _____

_____

_____

21. Of the two oceans, the (Atlantic, Pacific) Ocean has higher average surface salinities. Circle your answer.

22. Suggest a reason(s) for the difference in average surface salinities between the oceans.

_____

_____

_____

Figure 11 shows how ocean water salinity varies with depth at different latitudes. Use the figure to answer questions 23–26.

23. In general, salinity (increases, decreases) with depth in the equatorial and tropical regions and (increases, decreases) with depth at high latitudes. Circle your answers.

24. Why are the surface salinities higher than the deepwater salinities in the lower latitudes?

_____

_____

The *halocline* (*halo*-salt, *cline*-slope) is a layer of ocean water where there is a rapid change in salinity with depth.

25. Label the halocline on Figure 11. Where does it occur?

_____

26. Below the halocline the salinity of ocean water (increases rapidly, remains fairly constant, decreases rapidly). Circle your answer.

Figure 12 Lab setup for temperature–density experiment.

Step 4. Empty the cylinder and refill it with *hot* water.

Step 5. Add a test tube full of cold water and 2–3 drops of dye to some ice in a beaker. Stir the solution for a few seconds. Fill the test tube three-fourths full with some liquid (no ice) from your beaker. Pour this cold liquid *slowly* into the cylinder. Then record your observations.

Observations: _____

_____

_____

Step 6. Clean the glassware and return it along with the other materials to your instructor.

27. Questions 27a and 27b refer to the temperature–density experiment.

   a. Write a brief summary of your temperature–density experiment.

   _____

   _____

   _____

   b. Given equal salinities, (cold, warm) seawater would have the greatest density. Circle your answer.

Table 4 shows the average surface temperature and density of seawater at various latitudes. Using the data, plot a line on the graph in Figure 13 for temperature and a separate line for density using a different color. Then answer questions 28–30.

28. (Warm, Cool) surface temperatures and (high, low) surface densities occur in the equatorial regions. While at high latitudes, (warm, cool) surface temperatures and (high, low) surface densities are found. Circle your answers.

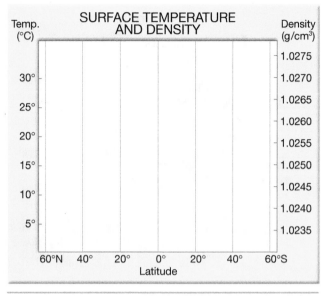

Figure 13   Graph for plotting surface temperatures and densities.

29. What is the reason for the fact that higher average surface densities are found in the Southern Hemisphere?

   _____

In question 18 you concluded that surface salinities were greatest at about latitudes 30°N and 30°S.

30. Refer to the density curve in Figure 13. What evidence supports the fact that the temperature of seawater is more of a controlling factor of density than salinity?

   _____

   _____

Figure 14 shows how ocean water temperature varies with depth at different latitudes. Use the figure to answer questions 31–33.

31. Temperature decreases most rapidly with depth at (high, low) latitudes. Circle your answer and give the reason that the decrease with depth is most rapid at these latitudes.

   _____

The layer of water where there is a rapid change of temperature with depth is called the *thermocline* (*thermo* = heat, *cline* = slope). The thermocline is a very important structure in the ocean because it creates a vertical barrier to many types of marine life.

Table 4   **Idealized Ocean Surface Water Temperatures and Densities at Various Latitudes**

LATITUDE	SURFACE TEMPERATURE (C°)	SURFACE DENSITY (g/cm³)
60°N	5	1.0258
40°	13	1.0259
20°	24	1.0237
0°	27	1.0238
20°	24	1.0241
40°	15	1.0261
60°S	2	1.0272

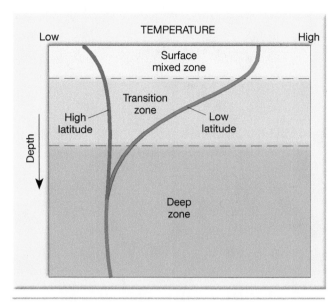

Figure 14 Ocean water temperature changes with depth at high and low latitudes.

32. Label the thermocline on Figure 14. Where does it occur?

_____

33. Below the thermocline the temperature of ocean water (increases rapidly, remains fairly constant, decreases rapidly). Circle your answer.

Oceanography on the Internet

Continue your exploration of the oceans by applying the concepts in this exercise to investigate real-time ocean water characteristics on the *Applications & Investigations in Earth Science* website at http://prenhall.com/earthsciencelab

Notes and calculations.

Introduction to Oceanography

Date Due: _____

Name: _____

Date: _____

Class: _____

After you have finished this exercise, complete the following questions. You may have to refer to the exercise for assistance or to locate specific answers. Be prepared to submit this summary/report to your instructor at the designated time.

1. Give the approximate latitude and longitude of the centers of each of the following water bodies.

   Mediterranean Sea: _____

   Sea of Japan: _____

   Indian Ocean: _____

2. Write a brief statement comparing the distribution of water and land in the Northern Hemisphere to the distribution in the Southern Hemisphere.

   _____

   _____.

3. On the ocean basin profile in Figure 15, label the continental shelf, continental slope, abyssal plain, seamounts, mid-ocean ridge, and deep-ocean trench.

4. List the names and depths of two Pacific Ocean trenches.

NAME	DEPTH
_____	_____
_____	_____

5. Explain how an echo sounder is used to determine the shape or topography of the ocean floor.

   _____

   _____

   _____

   _____

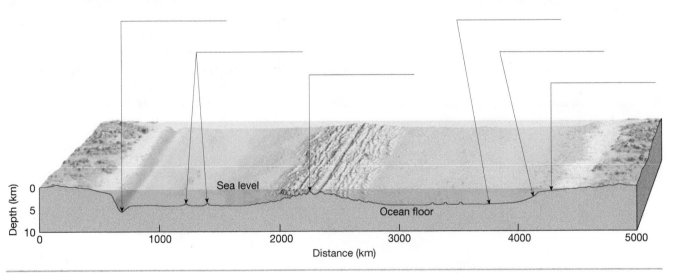

Figure 15 Hypothetical ocean basin.

6. The following are some short statements. Circle the most appropriate response.

   a. The higher the salinity of seawater, the (lower, higher) the density.

   b. The lower the temperature of seawater, the (lower, higher) the density.

   c. Surface salinity is greatest in (polar, subtropical, equatorial) regions.

   d. (Temperature, Salinity) has the greatest influence on the density of seawater.

   e. (Warm, Cold) seawater with (high, low) salinity would have the greatest density.

   f. Vertical movements of ocean water are most likely to begin in (equatorial, subtropical, polar) regions, because the surface water there is (most, least) dense.

7. Summarize the results of your salinity–density and temperature–density experiments.

   Salinity–density experiment: _____

   _____

   _____

   _____

   Temperature–density experiment: _____

   _____

   _____

   _____

8. Why is the surface salinity of an ocean higher in the subtropics than in the equatorial regions?

   _____

   _____

   _____

9. Given your understanding of the relation between ocean water temperature, salinity, and density, where in the Atlantic Ocean would you expect surface water to sink and initiate a subsurface flow? List the reason(s) for your choice(s).

   _____

   _____

   _____

   _____

10. Refer to the salinity–density experiment you conducted. Solution (A, B) had the greatest density. Circle your answer.

11. Describe the change in salinity *and* temperature with depth that occurs at low latitudes.

    Salinity: _____

    _____

    _____

    Temperature: _____

    _____

    _____

12. Are the following statements true or false? Circle your response. If the statement is false, correct the word(s) so that it reads as a true statement.

    T F a. The Atlantic Ocean covers the greatest area of all the world oceans.

    T F b. Continental shelves are part of the deep-ocean floor.

    T F c. Deep-ocean trenches are located in the middle of ocean basins.

    T F d. High evaporation rates in the subtropics cause the surface ocean water to have a lower than average salinity.

Waves, Currents, and Tides

The world's ocean waters are in constant motion via waves, currents, and tides. The immediate cause of each varies; however, the ultimate source of energy is the Sun. Investigating the causes, mechanics, and results of these ocean-water movements will provide a greater understanding of some important systems that operate over 70% of Earth's surface—the world oceans (Figure 1).

Objectives

After you have completed this exercise, you should be able to:

1. Explain how waves and currents are generated in the ocean.
2. Name the parts of a wave and describe the motion of water particles in a deepwater and shallow-water wave.
3. Use a formula to calculate wavelength, wave velocity, and wave period.
4. Explain why waves are refracted and what causes them to break and form surf.
5. Locate each of the major surface ocean currents.
6. List the names and characteristics of the principal deepwater masses.
7. Identify the features of erosion and deposition that occur along shorelines and explain how each is formed.
8. Explain the cause of tides and identify the different types of tides.

Materials

colored pencils   hand lens   calculator

Materials Supplied by Your Instructor

atlas or world wall map

Figure 1 Cliff undercut by wave erosion along the Oregon coast. (Photo by E. J. Tarbuck)

Terms

wave crest	surface current	estuary
wave trough	Coriolis effect	beach
wave height	density current	spit
wavelength	longshore current	tombolo
wave period	tidal current	baymouth bar
surf zone	emergent coast	diurnal tide
tsunami	wave-cut cliff	semidiurnal tide
refraction	platform	mixed tide
headland	submergent coast	

Waves

Most waves are set in motion when friction with wind begins rotating water particles in circular orbits (Figure 2). If you were to watch a ball floating on the surface, you would notice that while the wave form moves forward, the ball, and hence the water, does not. On the surface, as water particles reach the highest point in their circular orbits, a **wave crest** is formed, while particles at their lowest orbital points form **wave troughs**. **Wave height** is the vertical distance between the crest and trough of a wave.

Beneath the surface in deep water the circular orbits of water particles become progressively smaller with depth. At a depth equal to about half the **wavelength** (the horizontal distance separating two successive wave crests), the circular motion of water particles becomes negligible.

1. From Figure 2, select the letter that identifies each of the following.

	LETTER		LETTER
wave crest	_____	wavelength	_____
wave trough	_____	depth of negligible water particle motion	_____
wave height	_____	_____	

2. Below what depth would a submarine have to submerge so that it would not be swayed by surface waves with a wavelength of 24 meters?

   Below _____ meters

Wave Mechanics

In deep water, where the depth is greater than half the wavelength, the velocity (V) of a wave depends upon the **wave period** (T) (the time interval between successive wave crests, measured from a stationary point) and the wavelength (L). The mathematical equation that expresses the relation between these variables is velocity = wavelength divided by wave period ($V = L/T$).

As a wave approaches the shore and the depth of water becomes less than half the deepwater wavelength, the ocean bottom begins to interfere with the orbital motion of water particles, and the wave begins to "feel bottom" (Figure 2). Interference between the bottom and water particle motion causes changes to occur in the wave. At a depth of water equal to about one-twentieth of the deepwater wavelength [$(\frac{1}{20})L$ or $0.05L$], the top of the wave begins to fall forward and the wave breaks. In the **surf zone**, where waves are breaking and releasing energy, a significant amount of water is transported toward the shoreline.

3. What are three wind factors that determine the height, length, and period of waves?

   Factor 1: _____

   Factor 2: _____

   Factor 3: _____

   Refer to Figure 2 to answer questions 4–7.

4. The shape of the orbits of surface water particles in deepwater waves is (circular, elliptical). Near the shore in shallow water, the shapes become (circular, elliptical). Circle your answers.

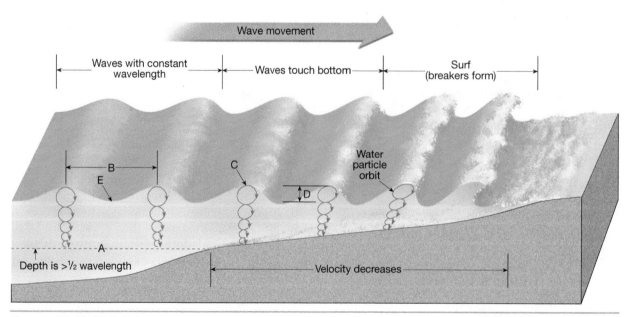

Figure 2 Deep- and shallow-water waves.

5. In shallow water, water particles in the wave crest are (ahead of, behind) those at the bottom of the wave.

6. As waves approach the shore in shallow water, their heights (increase, decrease) and the wavelength becomes (longer, shorter).

7. In the surf zone, water particles in the crest of a wave are (falling forward, standing still).

8. What would be the velocity of deepwater waves with a wavelength of 40 meters and a wave period of 6.3 seconds?

$$\text{Velocity} = \frac{\text{wavelength}(L)}{\text{wave period}(T)} = \frac{40 \text{ m}}{6.3 \text{ sec}}$$

$$= \underline{\hspace{2cm}} \text{m/sec}$$

9. What would be the wavelength of deepwater waves that have a period of 8 seconds and a velocity of 2 meters/sec? (*Hint: V × T = L*)

Wavelength(*L*) = _____ meters

a. What would be the *wave base* (depth below which water particle motion in the wave ceases) for the waves in question 9?

Wave base = _____ meters

b. The waves in question 9 will begin to break at a water depth of about (1, 3, 5) meter(s). Circle your answer.

10. What factor(s) determine the distance between where waves begin to break and the shoreline?

_____

11. Imagine that you are standing on the shore considering walking out into the surf zone where the waves are beginning to break, but you cannot swim. You estimate the wavelength of the incoming deepwater waves to be 80 meters. Would it be safe to walk out to where the waves are breaking? Explain how you arrived at your answer.

_____

_____

12. Along some shorelines, why does the water simply rise and fall rather than forming a surf zone?

_____

13. What effect will *breakwaters* (walls of concrete or rock built offshore and parallel to the beach) have on waves?

_____

Tsunamis (ocean waves produced by a submarine earthquake, sometimes mistakenly called "tidal waves") can have a wavelength of 125 miles and a wave period of 20 minutes.

14. If a tsunami had a wavelength of 125 miles and a period of 20 minutes, what would be its velocity?

Velocity = _____ miles per hour

Wave Refraction

Waves that approach the shore at an angle are **refracted** (bent) because that part of the wave that touches bottom first is slowed down, while the remaining part of the wave continues to move forward. Refraction causes most waves to reach the shore approximately parallel to the shoreline.

Figure 3 illustrates a map-view of a **headland** along a coastline with water depths shown by contour lines. Assume that waves, with a wavelength of 80 feet, are approaching the shoreline from the lower margin of the figure.

Use Figure 3 to answer questions 15–21.

15. The approaching waves will begin to touch bottom and slow down at a water depth of about (10, 20, 30, 40) feet. Circle your answer.

16. At a water depth of approximately (4, 8, 12, 16) feet, the waves will begin to break.

17. Indicate where the waves will begin to break with a dashed line. Write the words "surf zone" along the line.

18. Beginning with the wave shown, sketch a succession of lines to illustrate the wave refraction that will take place as the waves approach shore.

19. Use arrows to indicate where most of the wave energy will be concentrated as the waves are refracted and impact the shore.

20. Erosion by waves will be most severe (on the headland, in the bay). Circle your answer.

21. What effect will the concentrated energy from wave impact eventually have on the shape of the coastline?

_____

_____

Currents

Moving masses of water on the surface or within the ocean are called *currents.* The primary generating force for surface currents is wind, whereas deep-ocean circulation is a response to density differences among water masses.

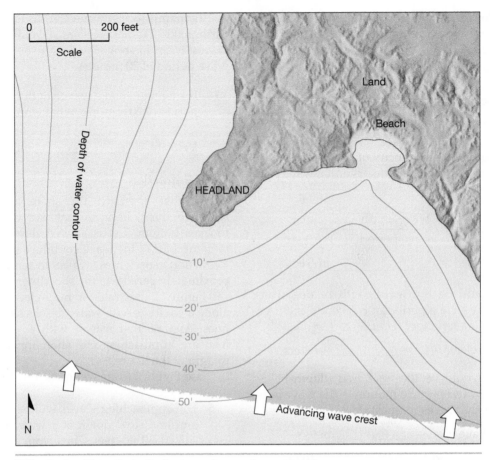

Figure 3 Coastline with depth of water contours and an approaching wave.

Surface Currents

Surface currents develop when friction between the moving atmosphere and the water causes the surface layer of the ocean to move as a single, large mass. Once set in motion, surface currents are influenced by the **Coriolis effect**, which deflects the path of the moving water to the right in the Northern Hemisphere and to the left in the Southern Hemisphere. *Warm currents* carry equatorial water toward the poles, while *cold currents* move water from higher latitudes toward the equator.

22. Many surface ocean currents flow with great persistence. On the world map, Figure 4, draw arrows representing each of the following principal surface ocean currents. Use an atlas or, if available, a large wall map that depicts surface currents as a reference. *Show warm currents with red arrows and cold currents with blue arrows.* To conserve space on the map, indicate the name of each current by writing the number that has been assigned to it.

PRINCIPAL SURFACE OCEAN CURRENTS

1. Equatorial	4. Canaries
2. Gulf Stream	5. Brazil
3. California	6. Benguela
7. Kuro Siwo	10. North Atlantic Drift
8. West Wind Drift	11. North Pacific Drift
9. Labrador	12. Peruvian

Using Figure 4, or a world map of surface ocean currents, answer questions 23–26.

23. Which surface ocean current travels completely around the globe, west to east, without interruption?

_____

24. Which surface ocean current flows along the eastern coast of the United States? The current is a (warm, cold) current. Circle your answer.

_____

25. What is the name of the surface ocean current located along the western coast of the United States? The current is a (warm, cold) current. Circle your answer.

_____

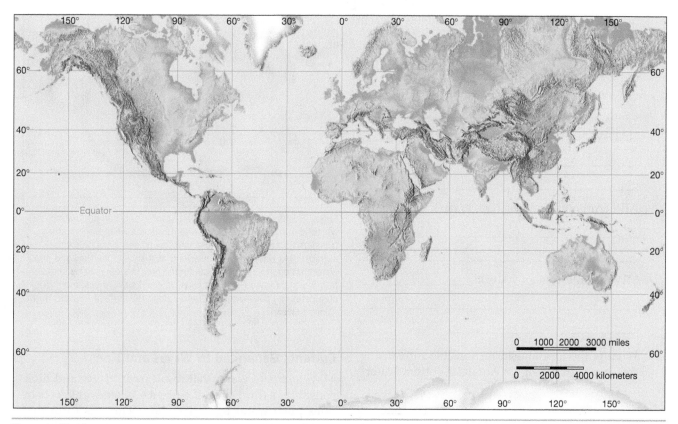

Figure 4 World map.

26. The general circulation of the surface currents in the North Atlantic Ocean is (clockwise, counterclockwise). In the South Atlantic, circulation is (clockwise, counterclockwise). Circle your answers.

Density Currents

Density currents result when water of greater density flows under or through water of a lower density. At any given depth, the density of water is influenced by its temperature and salinity—factors that you may have investigated in the exercise "Introduction to Oceanography."

Figure 5 is a cross section of the Atlantic Ocean illustrating the deep (thermohaline) circulation. Use the figure to answer questions 27 and 28.

27. After you examine their latitude of origin, describe the probable temperature and/or salini-

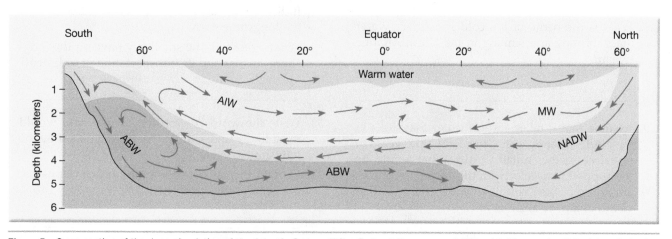

Figure 5 Cross section of the deep circulation of the Atlantic Ocean. (After Gerhard Neumann and Willard J. Pierson, Jr., *Principles of Physical Oceanography,* 1966. Reprinted by permission of Gerhard Neumann)

ty characteristics and general movements of each of the following water masses.

ABW (Antarctic Bottom Water): _____

_____

_____

NADW (North Atlantic Deep Water): _____

_____

_____

AIW (Antarctic Intermediate Water): _____

_____

_____

MW (Mediterranean Water): _____

_____

_____

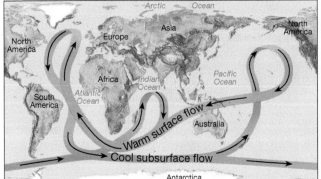

Figure 6 Idealized "conveyor belt" model of ocean circulation, which is initiated in the North Atlantic Ocean when warm water transfers its heat to the atmosphere, cools, and sinks below the surface. This water moves southward as a subsurface flow and joins water that encircles Antarctica. From here, this deep water spreads into the Indian and Pacific oceans, where it slowly rises and completes the conveyer as it travels along the surface into the North Atlantic Ocean.

28. What is the mechanism responsible for causing the very high density of Antarctic Bottom Water?

_____

_____

Deep-ocean circulation begins in high latitudes where water becomes cold and its salinity increases as sea ice forms. When this surface water becomes dense enough, it sinks and moves throughout the ocean basins in sluggish currents. Oceanographers estimate that after sinking from the surface of the ocean, deep waters will not reappear at the surface for an average of 500 to 2,000 years. A simplified model of deep-ocean circulation is similar to a conveyor belt that travels from the Atlantic Ocean through the Indian and Pacific oceans and back again (Figure 6). Use Figure 6 to answer questions 29 and 30.

29. What is the name of the cold subsurface water mass forming and sinking in the North Atlantic Ocean?

_____

30. Assume that it takes surface water that sinks in the North Atlantic near Greenland 1,000 years to resurface in the Indian Ocean. What would be the approximate velocity of the deep-ocean circulation from the North Atlantic to the Indian Ocean in km/yr and cms/hr?

_____ km(s)/yr

_____ cm(s)/hr

Currents Generated by Waves and Tides

Movements of water that result from waves and tides constitute a third class of currents. Whenever waves or tides push water against a shore, currents form that transport the water along the coast and return it seaward. Two of these currents are longshore currents and tidal currents.

Longshore currents form when waves strike the coast at an angle and the water moves in a zigzag pattern parallel to the shore in the surf zone. These currents transport tremendous amounts of sediment which, when deposited, form many types of coastal features.

Tidal currents, which reverse their direction of flow with each tide, submerge and then expose low-lying coastal zones.

In Figure 3 you completed a diagram illustrating wave refraction. Answer questions 31–34 by referring to Figure 3.

31. Indicate with arrows the probable directions of the longshore currents.

32. What effect will the small bay have on the longshore current and its transportation of sediment?

_____

33. Write the word "deposition" where you would most likely find sediment being deposited by the longshore current.

34. Explain the cause of the sandy beach deposit at the head of the small bay.

_____

_____

Shoreline Features

The nature of shorelines varies considerably from place to place. One way that geologists classify coasts is based upon changes that have occurred with respect to sea level. This very general classification divides coasts into two types, emergent and submergent.

Emergent coasts have been raised above the sea as a result of rising land or falling sea level and are characterized by **wave-cut cliffs** or **platforms**.

Submergent coasts, resulting from a rising sea level or subsiding land, are often irregular due to the fact that many river mouths are flooded and become **estuaries**.

Nevertheless, whether along the rugged New England coast or the steep coastlines of California, the effects of wave erosion and sediment deposition by currents produce many similar features. Some of the more common depositional features include **beaches**, **spits**, **tombolos**, and **baymouth bars**.

Features of Emergent and Submergent Coasts

Figure 7 illustrates several erosional and depositional features of emergent and submergent coastlines. Using Figure 7, complete questions 35–37.

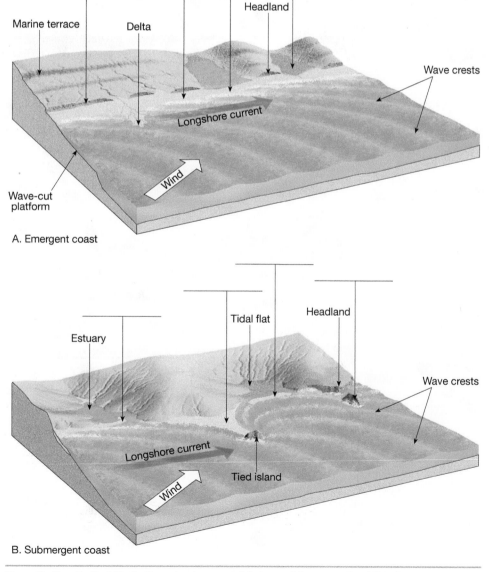

A. Emergent coast

B. Submergent coast

Figure 7 Hypothetical illustrations showing general features of **A.** emergent and **B.** submergent coastlines.

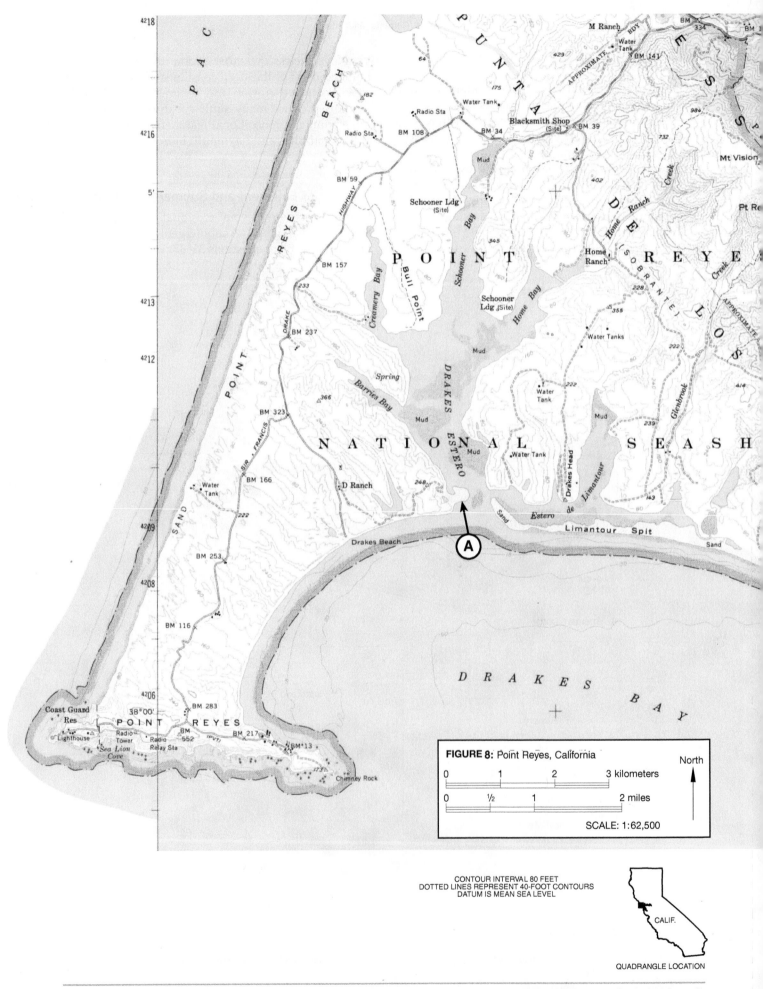

Figure 8   Portion of the Point Reyes, California, topographic map. (Map source: United States Department of the Interior, Geological Survey)

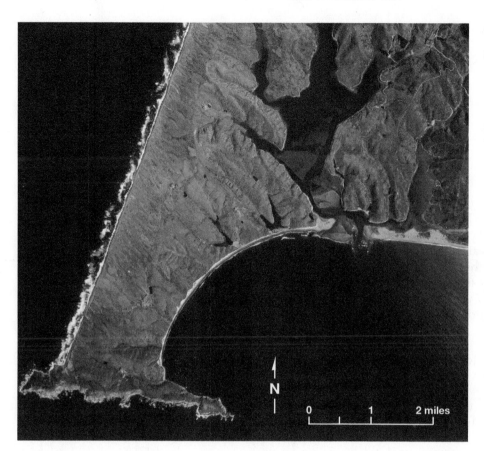

Figure 9 High-altitude false-color image of the Point Reyes area north of San Francisco, California. (Courtesy of USDA–ASCS)

N

0   1   2 miles

35. On Figure 7 identify each of the following coastal features by writing their name above the appropriate vertical line.

FEATURES CAUSED BY EROSION	FEATURES PRODUCED BY DEPOSITION	
wave-cut cliff	beach	baymouth bar
sea stack	spit	barrier island
	tombolo	

36. What is the purpose for constructing each of the following artificial features along a coast?

a *groin*: _____

a pair of *jetties*: _____

37. Draw and label a pair of jetties at the most appropriate location along the emergent coast illustrated in Figure 7A.

Identifying Coastal Features on a Topographic Map

Figure 8 is a portion of the Point Reyes, California, topographic map. Compare the map with the high-altitude image of the same area in Figure 9. Then use Figure 8, Figure 9, and Figure 7 to answer questions 38–44.

38. The features along the shoreline of Drakes Bay suggest that the coast is (emergent, submergent). Circle your answer.

39. Drakes Estero and other bays shown on the map are (estuaries, headlands).

40. Point Reyes, a typical headland, is undergoing severe wave erosion. What type of feature is Chimney Rock and the other rocks located off the shore of Point Reyes? How have they formed?

_____

_____

41. Several depositional features in Drakes Bay are related to the movement of sediment by longshore currents. The feature labeled A on the map is one of these features, called a (spit, tombolo).

42. Using a large arrow, indicate the direction of the current in the vicinity of Limantour Spit.

43. Assume a groin is constructed by the word "Limantour" on Limantour Spit. On which side of the groin, east or west, will sand accumulate? What will be the effect on the opposite side of the groin?

_____

_____

44. What is the probable origin of the "U-shaped" lake east of D Ranch?

_____

_____

Tides

Tides are the cyclical rise and fall of sea level caused by the gravitational attraction of the Moon and, to a lesser extent, by the Sun. Gravitational pull creates a bulge in the ocean on the side of Earth nearest the Moon and on the opposite side of Earth from the Moon. Tides develop as the rotating Earth moves through these bulges causing periods of high and low water. Using tidal information from many sources, tides are classified into three types:

- **Diurnal** (*diurnal* = daily) **tides** are characterized by a single high tide and a single low tide each tidal day.
- **Semidiurnal** (*semi* = twice, *diurnal* = daily) **tides** exhibit two high tides and two low tides each tidal day.
- **Mixed tides** are similar to semidiurnal tides except that they are characterized by large inequalities in high water heights, low water heights, or both (Figure 10).

Identifying Types of Tides

Tidal curves for the month of September at several locations are illustrated in Figure 11. Use the figure to answer questions 45–47.

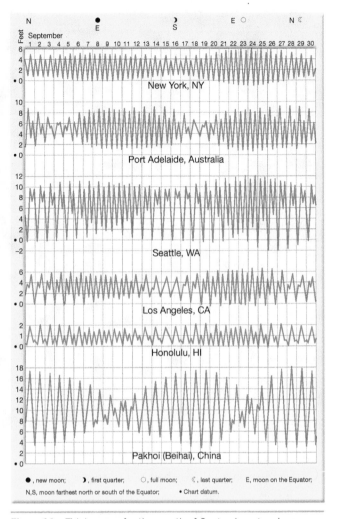

Figure 11 Tidal curves for the month of September at various locations. (Source: U.S. Navy Hydrograph Office, *Oceanography*, U.S. Government Printing Office, 1966)

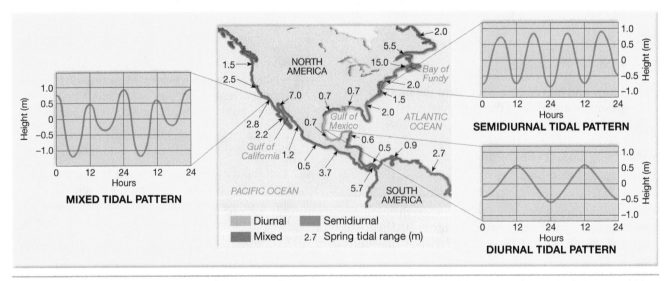

Figure 10 Tidal patterns and their occurrence along North and Central American coasts. A diurnal tidal pattern (*lower right*) shows one high and low tide each tidal day. A semidiurnal pattern (*upper right*) shows two highs and lows of approximately equal heights during each tidal day. A mixed tidal pattern (left) shows two highs and lows of unequal heights during each tidal day.

45. Classify each of the tidal curves shown in Figure 11 as to the most appropriate type.

    Diurnal tides occur at: _____

    _____

    Semidiurnal tides: _____

    _____

    Mixed tides: _____

    _____

46. Of the locations you classified as having a *mixed* tide, (Port Adelaide, Seattle, Los Angeles) had the greatest inequality between successive low water heights on September 5. Circle your answer.

47. Write a general statement comparing the type of tide that occurs along the Pacific coast of the United States to the type found along the Atlantic coast.

    _____

    _____

Tidal Variations

In Figure 11, notice that during the month of September, at any given location, the heights of the tides were not constant. Two important factors that influence this variation are (1) the alignment of the Sun, Earth, and Moon, and (2) the distance between Earth and the Moon. Although these two controls are significant, they alone cannot be used to predict the height or time of actual tides at a particular place. Other factors, such as the shape of the coastline and the configuration of ocean basins, are also important. Consequently, tides at various locations respond differently to the tide-producing forces.

Use Figure 11 to answer questions 48–53.

48. As shown in Figure 11, the *tidal range* (difference in height between high tide and the following low tide) at any one location (changes, remains the same) throughout September. Circle your answer.

    The lunar phases for the month are shown at the top of the figure (new moon on the 8th and full moon on the 23rd of the month).

49. What general relation seems to exist between the phases of the Moon and the tidal ranges at New York?

    _____

    _____

50. Explain the cause of *spring tides* and *neap tides*. Sketch a diagram showing the relative positions of the Earth, Moon, and Sun, viewed from above, that would cause each situation.

Spring tide

Spring tides: _____

_____

_____

Neap tide

Neap tides: _____

_____

_____

51. On Figure 11, label the times of spring tide and times of neap tide for New York.

52. Do the tides at Pakhoi, China, have the same relations to the lunar phases as those that occur at New York? What are some other factors that may be influencing the tides at Pakhoi?

    _____

    _____

97

Table 1 Tidal Data for Long Beach, New York, January 2003

	TIMES ARE LISTED IN LOCAL STANDARD TIME (LST) — ALL HEIGHTS ARE IN FEET							
DAY	TIME	HEIGHT	TIME	HEIGHT	TIME	HEIGHT	TIME	HEIGHT
1	05:45 A.M.	5.5	12:16 P.M.	−0.7	06:12 P.M.	4.4	—	—
2	12:18 A.M.	−0.5	06:35 A.M.	5.6	01:07 P.M.	−0.8	07:03 P.M.	4.4
3	01:10 A.M.	−0.5	07:23 A.M.	5.5	01:56 P.M.	−0.8	07:53 P.M.	4.4
4	01:59 A.M.	−0.4	08:11 A.M.	5.4	02:42 P.M.	−0.7	08:42 P.M.	4.3
5	02:45 A.M.	−0.2	08:59 A.M.	5.1	03:25 P.M.	−0.5	09:32 P.M.	4.2
6	03:30 A.M.	0.0	09:47 A.M.	4.8	04:07 P.M.	−0.3	10:23 P.M.	4.0
7	04:14 A.M.	0.3	10:35 A.M.	4.6	04:49 P.M.	−0.1	11:12 P.M.	3.9
8	05:01 A.M.	0.6	11:22 A.M.	4.3	05:32 P.M.	0.2	11:59 P.M.	3.9
9	05:54 A.M.	0.8	12:09 P.M.	4.0	06:18 P.M.	0.4	—	—
10	12:45 A.M.	3.9	06:56 A.M.	0.9	12:57 P.M.	3.7	07:10 P.M.	0.5
11	01:31 A.M.	3.9	07:59 A.M.	0.9	01:47 P.M.	3.5	08:02 P.M.	0.5
12	02:19 A.M.	4.0	08:57 A.M.	0.8	02:41 P.M.	3.4	08:53 P.M.	0.5
13	03:10 A.M.	4.1	09:50 A.M.	0.6	03:39 P.M.	3.5	09:41 P.M.	0.4
14	04:02 A.M.	4.3	10:38 A.M.	0.3	04:34 P.M.	3.6	10:28 P.M.	0.2
15	04:51 A.M.	4.6	11:26 A.M.	0.1	05:23 P.M.	3.7	11:15 P.M.	0.1
16	05:36 A.M.	4.8	12:12 P.M.	−0.1	06:08 P.M.	3.9	—	—
17	12:02 A.M.	−0.1	06:17 A.M.	5.0	12:57 P.M.	−0.3	06:51 P.M.	4.1
18	12:49 A.M.	−0.2	06:58 A.M.	5.1	01:40 P.M.	−0.5	07:32 P.M.	4.2
19	01:35 A.M.	−0.4	07:38 A.M.	5.2	02:22 P.M.	−0.6	08:15 P.M.	4.3
20	02:20 A.M.	−0.4	08:21 A.M.	5.2	03:30 P.M.	−0.7	09:01 P.M.	4.4

(Source: Center for Operational Oceanographic Products and Services, National Oceanographic and Atmospheric Association, National Ocean Service.)

At some locations, tidal power is being considered as a means of generating electricity.

53. Suggest two criteria that a bay must meet before its tidal energy can be economically harnessed.

   Criterion 1: _____

   Criterion 2: _____

Examining Tidal Data

Table 1 presents January 2003 tidal data for Long Beach, New York. Accurately plot the data on the graph in Figure 12. After you have plotted the data, answer questions 54–58.

54. What type of tide occurs at Long Beach, New York? What fact(s) support your conclusion?

   _____

   _____

   _____

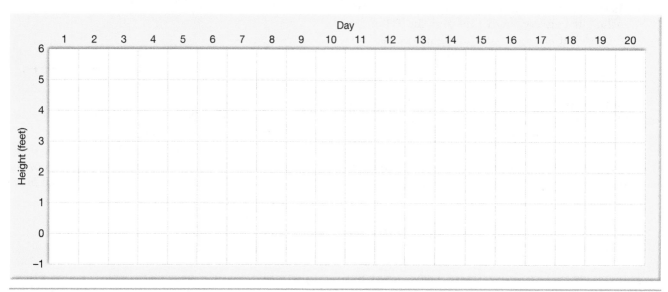

Figure 12 Tidal curve for Long Beach, New York

55. The greatest tidal range occurs on day _____, while the smallest range is on day _____.

56. Selecting from the tidal curves in Figure 11, the tides at Long Beach are most like those at:

_____

Examine closely the association between the tides shown for the city you selected in question 56 and the phases of the Moon depicted at the top of Figure 11.

57. Using Figure 11 as a reference, label the most likely lunar phases associated with the tidal curve above the appropriate days on Figure 12.

58. Using Table 1 and Figure 12, assume that at 9:00 A.M. on January 5, a boat was anchored near a beach in 4 feet of water. When the owner returned at 3:30 P.M., the boat was resting on sand. What had happened? Approximately how long did the owner have to wait to sail the boat away from the area?

_____

_____

_____

Waves, Currents, and Tides on the Internet

Continue your exploration of waves and tides by completing the corresponding online activity on the *Applications & Investigations in Earth Science* website at http://prenhall.com/earthsciencelab

Notes and calculations.

Waves, Currents, and Tides

Date Due: _____

Name: _____

Date: _____

Class: _____

After you have finished this exercise, complete the following questions. You may have to refer to the exercise for assistance or to locate specific answers. Be prepared to submit this summary/report to your instructor at the designated time.

1. On Figure 13 sketch a profile view of deep- and shallow-water waves approaching a shore. Label all parts and measurements of a typical wave. Also, illustrate the motion of several water particles at increasing depths in both a deep- and shallow-water wave.

2. What will happen to the shapes of waves as they approach a headland that is surrounded by shallow water?

   _____ The height wave will increase _____

3. Describe the formation and appearance of each of the following features:

   Spit: _is a long, that narrow into_
   ridge ofan deposited materials
   that extends from the mainland
   into the sea

   Stack: _land form consisting of a steep and_
   often vertical colum or colums of rock
   in the sea near a coast

   Tombolo: _is a deposition landform in_
   which an island is attached to
   the mainland by a narrow piece of land

   Estuary: _enclosed coastal body of_
   brackish water with one or more
   rivers or streams flowing into it

4. Refer to Figure 8. What types of coastal features are Point Reyes, Drakes Estero, and Chimney Rock?

   Point Reyes: _Sea cliffs_

   Drakes Estero: _estuary_

   Chimney Rock: _Sea stack_

5. The circulation of the surface currents in the South Atlantic Ocean is (clockwise, counterclockwise). Circle your answer.

wave motion

Figure 13 Deepwater waves approaching a shallow coast.

6. What are the names of the surface currents that are located along the east and west coasts of the United States? Is each a warm or a cold current?

East coast: _____

West coast: _____

7. List the characteristics and describe the movement of the following deep-ocean water masses in the Atlantic Ocean.

NADW: _lighter____water_____

_____

ABW: _heavier____water_____

_____

8. Spring tides are most likely to occur during which lunar phase(s)?

_full____moons____and____new____moon_

9. Which of the tidal curves illustrated in Figure 11 exhibits the greatest tidal range?

_____

10. Refer to Figure 11. Of the three types of tides, name the type that occurs at each of the following locations.

Pakhoi: _____

Honolulu: _____

New York: _____

11. Referring to question 54 of the exercise, what type of tide occurs at Long Beach, New York? Describe this type of tide.

_____

_____

_____

Introduction to Aerial Photographs and Topographic Maps

Aerial photographs, satellite images, and topographic maps are important research tools that provide insight into the various processes that shape the surface of the land. Each is an indispensable method for reducing vast amounts of data to a scale that can be easily managed. The ability of an Earth scientist to effectively interpret and use these tools is essential to identifying and understanding Earth features.

Objectives

After you have completed this exercise, you should be able to:

1. Use a stereoscope to view a stereogram, a pair of aerial photographs.
2. Explain what a topographic map is and how it can be used to study landforms.
3. Use map scales to determine distances.
4. Determine the latitude and longitude of a place from a topographic map.
5. Use the Public Land Survey system to locate features.
6. Explain how contour lines are drawn and be able to use contours to determine elevation, relief, and slope of the land.
7. Construct a simple contour map.
8. Construct a topographic profile.

Materials

ruler   hand lens

Materials Supplied by Your Instructor

stereoscope   United States and world
string   wall maps
topographic map

Terms

topographic map	Public Land	section
stereoscope	Survey	contour line
stereogram	base line	contour interval
datum	principal	index contour
quadrangle	meridian	bench mark
magnetic	township	slope
declination	range	relief
map scale	congressional	topographic
fractional scale	township	profile
graphic scale		

Aerial Photographs

Aerial photographs are useful for geological, environmental, agricultural, and related studies. Photographs of the same feature, when taken sequentially and overlapped, can be viewed in three dimensions through a viewer called a **stereoscope.**

To view a stereoscopic aerial photograph, called a **stereogram,** the stereoscope is placed directly over the line separating any two photos of the same feature (Figure 1). As you look through a stereoscope, it may have to be moved around slightly until the image appears in three dimensions. The observed heights will be vertically exaggerated, and the difference in heights you see through the stereoscope will not be the same as the actual difference in heights on the land.

To provide some practice viewing stereograms, obtain a stereoscope from your instructor, unfold it, and center it over the line that separates the two aerial photographs of the volcanic cone in Figure 2. As you view the photographs, adjust the stereoscope until the cone appears in three dimensions. You may have to be patient until your eyes focus.

Use the stereogram in Figure 2 to answer questions 1–5.

1. Identify and label the crater at the summit of the volcano.

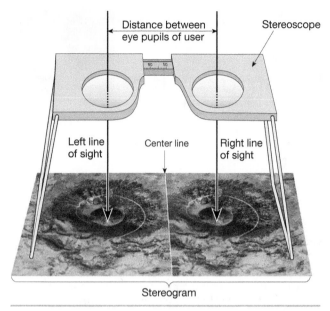

Figure 1 Aligning a stereoscope to view a stereogram.

2. Outline and label the lava flow, located at the intersection of the two coordinates, 1.5 and A.8, at the base of the volcano.

3. What is the white, curved feature that extends from the base of the cone to its summit?

4. Mark the highest point on the volcano with an "X."

5. Assume the summit of the volcanic cone is 1,500 feet above the surrounding land. While viewing the cone through the stereoscope, draw lines around the volcano at approximately 400-foot intervals above the local surface.

In addition to aerial photographs, beginning in the early 1970s, the United States began launching several satellites that systematically collect images of Earth's surface using a variety of remote sensing techniques.

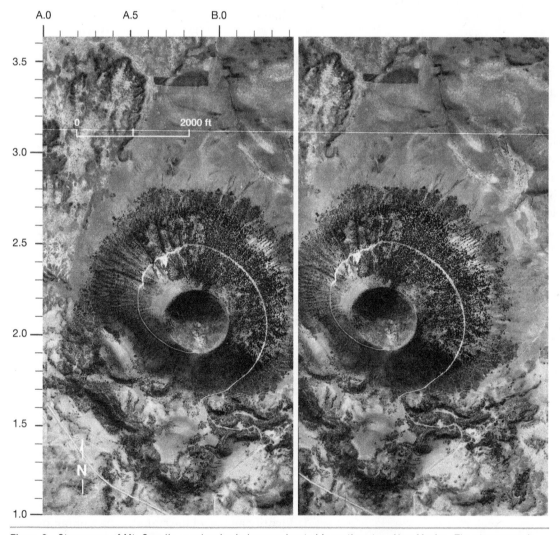

Figure 2 Stereogram of Mt. Capulin, a volcanic cinder cone located in northeastern New Mexico. The stereogram is composed from two overlapping aerial photographs taken from an altitude of approximately 16,000 feet. To view the three-dimensional image of the volcano, center a stereoscope over the line that separates the two photographs. Then, while looking through the stereoscope, adjust the stereoscope until the image appears in three dimensions. (Courtesy of U.S. Geological Survey)

Figure 3 Satellite image of a portion of the delta of the Mississippi River in May 2001. The image covers an area of 54 × 57 kilometers. For the past 600 years or so, the main flow of the river has been along its present course, extending southeast from New Orleans. During that span, the delta advanced into the Gulf of Mexico at a rate of about 10 kilometers (6 miles) per century. For a more detailed investigation of satellite images see the Internet activities at the URL listed at the end of this exercise. (Photo courtesy of NASA)

The ability of the images to be computer manipulated and enhanced has made a tremendous amount of new data available to Earth scientists (Figure 3). (Further investigations of satellite imagery can be found at the URL indicated at the end of this exercise.)

Topographic Maps

One type of map, the **topographic map,** is most useful when investigating the many kinds of landforms that exist on Earth's surface.

Topography means "the shape of the land." Each topographic map shows, to scale, the width, length, and variable height of the land above a **datum** or reference plane—generally average sea level. The maps, which are also referred to as **quadrangles,** are two-dimensional representations of the three-dimensional surface of Earth. Their primary value to the Earth scientist is for determining locations, landform types, elevations, and other physical data.

Topographic maps have been produced by the United States Geological Survey (USGS) since the late 1800s. Today, a vast area of the United States has been accurately portrayed on these commercially available maps.

To facilitate their use, topographic maps follow a similar format. In addition to standard colors and

symbols, each contains information about where the area mapped is located, the date when the mapping was done or revised, scale, north arrow, and the names of adjoining quadrangle maps.

To help understand the basics of topographic maps, obtain a copy of a topographic map from your instructor and examine it. You will use this map to answer specific groups of questions that follow. PLEASE DO NOT WRITE OR MARK ON THE MAP.

General Map Information

Every topographic map contains useful information printed in its margin. Locate and record the following information for your map.

Each topographic map is assigned a name for reference. The name of a topographic map is located in the upper-right corner of the map.

6. What is the name of your map?

   Map name: _____

Notice the small reference map and compass arrow in the lower margin of the map.

7. In what part of the state (north, southwest, etc.) is the area covered by your map located?

   _____

The names of adjoining maps are given along the four margins and four corners of the map.

8. What is the name of the map that adjoins the northeast corner of your map?

   Adjoining map: _____

Information about when the area was surveyed and the map published is provided in the margin of the map.

9. When was the area surveyed? When was the map published? If the map has been revised, when was the revision completed?

   Surveyed: _____ Published: _____ Revised: _____

Since the geographic North Pole and North Magnetic Pole of Earth do not coincide, the north arrow on a topographic map often shows the difference between true north (TN) and magnetic north (MN), the direction a compass would point, for the area represented. This difference in degrees is called the **magnetic declination.**

10. What is the magnetic declination of the area shown on your map?

    Magnetic declination: _____

Map Colors and Symbols

Each symbol and color used on a U.S. Geological Survey topographic map has a meaning. Refer to the list of standard U.S. Geological Survey topographic map symbols.

Using the standard map symbols as a guide, locate examples of various types of roads, buildings, and streams on the topographic map supplied by your instructor.

11. In general, what color(s) are used for the following types of features?

Highways and roads: _____

Buildings: _____

Urban areas: _____

Wooded areas: _____

Water features: _____

Map Scale

Many people have built or seen scale model airplanes or cars that are miniature representations of the actual objects. Maps are similar in that they are "scale models" of Earth's surface. Each map will have a **map scale** that expresses the relation between distance on the map to the true distance on Earth's surface. Different map scales depict an area on Earth with more or less detail. On a topographic map, scale is usually indicated in the lower margin and is expressed in two ways.

Fractional scale (e.g., 1/24,000 or 1:24,000) means that a distance of 1 unit on the map represents a distance of 24,000 of the *same* units on the surface of Earth. For example, one inch on the map equals 24,000 inches on Earth, or one centimeter on the map equals 24,000 centimeters on Earth. Maps with small fractional scales (fractions with large numbers in the denominator; e.g., 1/250,000) cover

large areas. Those with large fractional scales (fractions with small numbers in the denominator; e.g., 1/1,000) cover small areas. The United States Geological Survey publishes maps at various scales to meet both the need for broad coverage and detail (see Figures 4 and 5).

Graphic, or **bar, scale** is a bar that is divided into segments that show the relation between distance on the map to actual distance on Earth (Figure 6). Scales showing miles, feet, and kilometers are generally included. The left side of the bar is often divided into fractions to allow for more accurate measurement of distance. The graphic scale is more useful than the fractional scale for measuring distances between points. Graphic scales can be used to make your own "map ruler" for measuring distances on the map using a piece of paper or string.

12. Examine your topographic map as well as the large wall maps in the laboratory and write out the fractional scale for each in the following space. Then answer questions 12a and 12b.

Topographic map: _____ : _____

Wall map of the United States (if available):

_____ : _____

World map (if available):

_____ : _____

a. Which of the three maps has the smallest scale (largest denominator in the fractional scale)?

_____

b. Which of the three maps covers more square miles?

_____

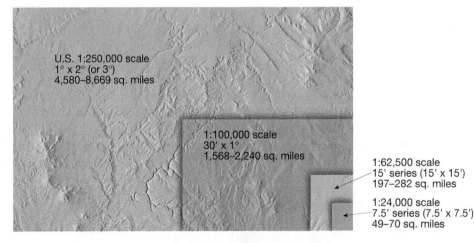

Figure 4 Standard U.S. Geological Survey topographic map scales, sizes, and coverage.

U.S. 1:250,000 scale
1° x 2° (or 3°)
4,580–8,669 sq. miles

1:100,000 scale
30' x 1°
1,568–2,240 sq. miles

1:62,500 scale
15' series (15' x 15')
197–282 sq. miles

1:24,000 scale
7.5' series (7.5' x 7.5')
49–70 sq. miles

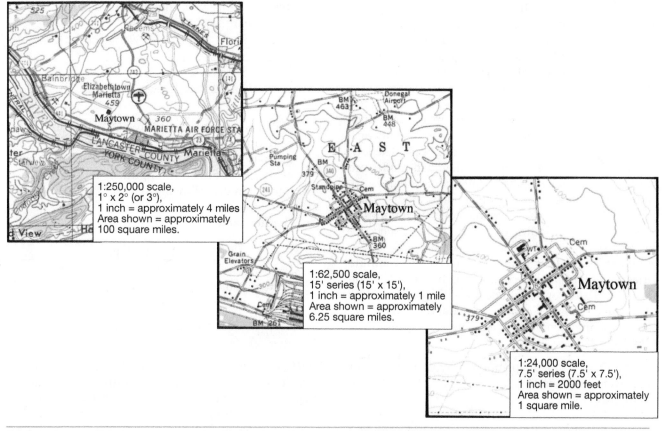

1:250,000 scale,
1° x 2° (or 3°),
1 inch = approximately 4 miles
Area shown = approximately
100 square miles.

1:62,500 scale,
15' series (15' x 15'),
1 inch = approximately 1 mile
Area shown = approximately
6.25 square miles.

1:24,000 scale,
7.5' series (7.5' x 7.5'),
1 inch = 2000 feet
Area shown = approximately
1 square mile.

Figure 5 Portions of three topographic maps of the same area showing the effect that different map scales have on the detail illustrated.

13. Depending on the map scale, one inch on a topographic map represents various distances on Earth. Convert the following scales.

SCALE	1 INCH ON THE MAP REPRESENTS
1 : 24,000	_____ feet on Earth
1 : 63,360	_____ mile(s) on Earth
1 : 250,000	_____ miles on Earth

14. Use the graphic scale provided on your topographic map to construct a "map ruler" in miles, and measure the following distances that are represented on the map.

Width of the map along the south edge = _____ miles

Length of the map along the east edge = _____ miles

15. How many square miles are represented on your topographic map? (*Hint:* The area of a rectangle is calculated using the formula, area = width × length.)

Map area equals _____ square miles

Location

One of the most useful functions of a topographic map is determining the precise location of a feature on Earth's surface. Two frequently used methods for designating location are (1) latitude and longitude to determine the location of a point and (2) the **Public Land Survey** (PLS) system to define an area. Because topographic maps

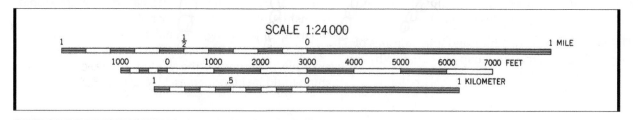

SCALE 1:24 000

1   ½   0   1 MILE

1000   0   1000   2000   3000   4000   5000   6000   7000 FEET

1   .5   0   1 KILOMETER

Figure 6 Typical graphic scale.

are very accurate, both methods of location can be used to provide information helpful to engineers, surveyors, realtors, and others. A third method, the Universal Transverse Mercator (UTM) grid, is investigated at the website located at the URL listed at the end of this exercise.

Latitude and Longitude. Topographic maps are bounded by parallels of latitude on the north and south, and meridians of longitude on the east and west. The latitudes and longitudes covered by the quadrangles are printed at the four corners of the map in degrees (°), minutes ('), and seconds (") and are indicated at intervals along the margins. Maps that cover 15 minutes of latitude and 15 minutes of longitude are called *15-minute series topographic maps,* and although no longer produced by the USGS are still available. A $7\frac{1}{2}$-minute series topographic map covers $7\frac{1}{2}$-minutes of latitude and $7\frac{1}{2}$-minutes of longitude (see Figure 4). [*Note:* There are 60 minutes of arc in one degree and 60 seconds of arc in one minute of arc. Therefore, $\frac{1}{2}$-minute is the same as 30 seconds.]

Use the topographic map supplied by your instructor to answer questions 16–22. PLEASE DO NOT WRITE OR MARK ON THE MAPS.

16. What are the latitudes of the southern edge and northern edge of the map to the nearest $\frac{1}{2}$ minute of latitude?

    Latitude of southern edge: _____

    Latitude of northern edge: _____

17. How many total minutes of latitude does the map cover?

    _____ minutes of latitude

18. What are the longitudes of the eastern edge and western edge of the map to the nearest $\frac{1}{2}$ minute of longitude?

    Longitude of eastern edge: _____

    Longitude of western edge: _____

19. How many total minutes of longitude does the map cover?

    _____ minutes of longitude

20. The map is a _____-minute series topographic map because it covers _____ minutes of latitude and _____ minutes of longitude.

21. The total minutes of latitude and total minutes of longitude covered by the map are equal. Why is

the appearance of the map rectangular rather than square?

_____

_____

22. Your instructor will supply you with the names of two features (school, church, etc.) located on the map. Write the name of each feature, as well as its latitude and longitude to the nearest minute, in the following spaces.

    Feature name: _____

    Latitude: _____ Longitude: _____

    Feature name: _____

    Latitude: _____ Longitude: _____

Public Land Survey. The Public Land Survey (PLS) provides a precise method for identifying the location of land in most states west of the Appalachian Mountains by establishing a grid system that systematically subdivides the land area (Figure 7). The PLS begins at an initial point (generally there are one or more initial points for each state that utilizes the PLS). An east–west line, called a **base line,** and a north–south line, called a **principal meridian,** extend through the initial point and provide the basis of the grid (see Figures 7 and 8).

Horizontal lines at six-mile intervals that parallel the base line establish east–west tracts, called **townships.** Each township is numbered north and south from the base line. The first horizontal six-mile-wide tract north of the base line is designated Township One North (T1N), the second T2N, etc. Vertical lines at six-mile intervals that parallel the principal meridian define north–south tracts, called **ranges.** Each range is numbered east and west of the principal meridian. The first vertical six-mile-wide tract west of the principal meridian is designated Range One West (R1W), the second R2W, etc. *On a topographic map, the townships and ranges covered by the map are printed in red along the margins.*

The intersection of a township and a range defines a six-mile-by-six-mile rectangle, called a **congressional township,** which may or may not coincide with a civil township. Each congressional township is identified by referring to its township and range numbers. For example, in Figure 7A, the shaded congressional township would be identified as T1N, R4W.

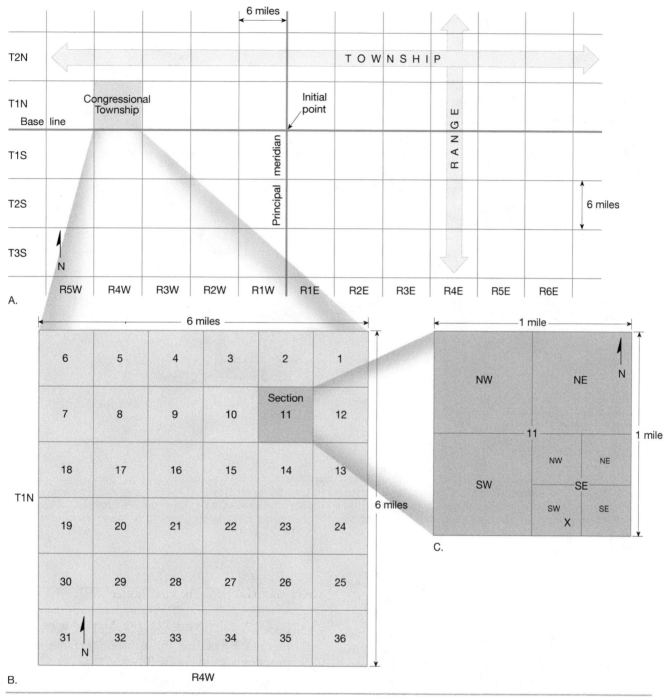

Figure 7 The Public Land Survey system (PLS).

Each congressional township is divided into 36 one-mile-square parcels of land, called **sections,** with each section containing 640 acres. Sections are numbered beginning with number one in the northeast corner of the congressional township and ending with number 36 in the southeast corner (Figure 7B). The shaded section of land in Figure 7B would be designated as Section 11, T1N, R4W. *On a topographic map, the sections are outlined and their numbers are printed in red.*

For more detailed descriptions, sections may be subdivided into halves, quarters, or quarters of a quarter (Figure 7C). Each of these subdivisions are identified by their compass position. For example, the forty acre area designated with the letter X in Figure 7C would be described as the $SW\frac{1}{4}$ (southwest $\frac{1}{4}$), of the $SE\frac{1}{4}$ (southeast $\frac{1}{4}$) of Section 11. Hence, the complete locational description of the area marked with the letter X would be $SW\frac{1}{4}$, $SE\frac{1}{4}$ Sec. 11, T1N, R4W.

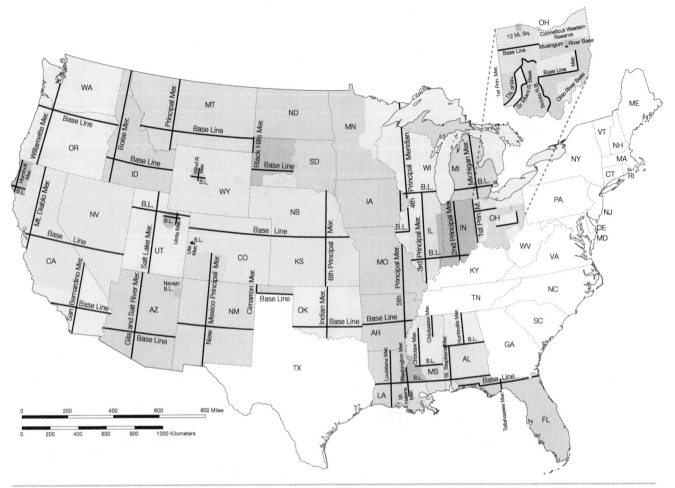

Figure 8 Regions in the conterminous United States that utilize the Public Land Survey (PLS) system. The unshaded areas (the original thirteen states and five others, plus Texas) were, for the most, settled prior to the establishment of the PLS in the late 1700s and utilize a variety of less structured systems (often referred to as "metes and bounds" descriptions) for designating land. (U.S. Department of Interior, Bureau of Land Management)

By convention, in the description the smallest subdivision is given first and the township number precedes the range number.

Figure 9 illustrates a hypothetical area that has been surveyed using the Public Land Survey system. Figure 9A is a township and range diagram, 9B represents a congressional township within the township and range system, and Figure 9C is a section of the congressional township. Use Figures 9A–9C to complete questions 23–25.

23. Use the PLS system to label the townships, ranges, and sections in Figure 9A and 9B with their proper designation.

24. Follow each of the letters. A through D, through Figure 9C–9A and write the PLS location description of each in the following spaces. As an example, letter A has already been done.

A: <u>NW</u> $\frac{1}{4}$, <u>SW</u> $\frac{1}{4}$, Sec. <u>8</u>, T <u>3N</u>, R <u>4W</u>

B: _____ $\frac{1}{4}$, _____ $\frac{1}{4}$, Sec. _____, T _____, R _____

C: _____ $\frac{1}{4}$, _____ $\frac{1}{4}$, Sec. _____, T _____, R _____

D: _____ $\frac{1}{4}$, _____ $\frac{1}{4}$, Sec. _____, T _____, R _____

25. Locate each of the areas described below on Figure 9 by placing the appropriate letter in the proper places in Figure 9A–9C.

E: SW$\frac{1}{4}$ SW$\frac{1}{4}$ Sec. 5, T5N, R3E

F: SE$\frac{1}{4}$, NE$\frac{1}{4}$, Sec. 34, T4S, R7W

Use the topographic map supplied by your instructor to answer questions 26–29. PLEASE DO NOT WRITE OR MARK ON THE MAPS.

26. List the townships and ranges represented on the map.

Townships: _____

Ranges: _____

27. To reach the principal meridian that was used to survey the land represented on the map, people

110

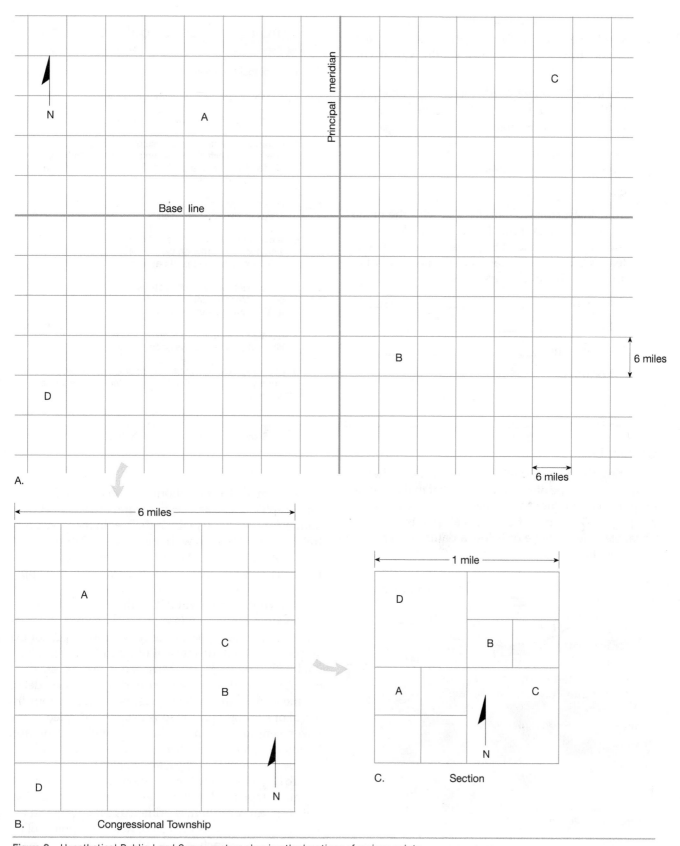

Figure 9 Hypothetical Public Land Survey system showing the locations of various points.

living within the area would have to travel (eastward, westward). To reach the base line, they would travel to the (north, south). Circle your answers.

28. What is the section, township, and range at each of the following locations on the map?

Exact center of the map:

Sec. _____, T _____, R _____

Extreme NE corner of the map:

Sec. _____, T _____, R _____

29. Your instructor will supply you with the names of three features (school, church, etc.) located on the map. Using the PLS system, write each of the feature's complete location to the nearest $\frac{1}{4}$ of a $\frac{1}{4}$ section in the following spaces.

Feature name: _____

Location: _____

Feature name: _____

Location: _____

Feature name: _____

Location: _____

Contour Lines

Depicting the height or elevation of the land, thereby showing the shape of landforms, is what makes a topographic map unique. A **contour line** is a line drawn on a topographic map that connects all points that have equal elevations above or below a datum or reference plane on Earth's surface (Figure 10). The reference

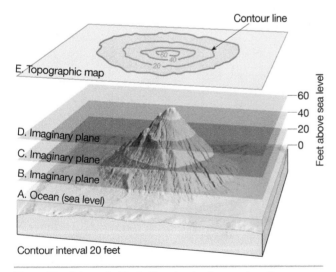

Figure 10 Schematic illustration showing how contour lines are determined when topographic maps are constructed. **A** is the ocean surface. **B** is an imaginary plane 20 feet above the ocean that intersects the land. **C** is an imaginary plane 40 feet above the ocean that intersects the land. **D** is an imaginary plane 60 feet above the ocean that intersects the land. **E** is the topographic map that results when the contour lines that mark where the imaginary planes intersect the surface are drawn on a map.

GENERAL RULES FOR CONTOUR LINES

1. A contour line connects points of equal elevation.

2. A contour line never branches or splits.

3. Steep slopes are shown by closely spaced contours.

4. Contour lines never cross, except to show an overhanging cliff. (To show an overhanging cliff, the hidden contours are dashed. Contour lines can also merge to form a single line along a vertical cliff.)

5. Hills are represented by a concentric series of closed contour lines.

6. A concentric series of closed contours with hachure marks on the downhill side represents a closed depression.

7. When contour lines cross streams or dry stream channels, they form a "V" that points upstream.

8. Contour lines that occur on opposite sides of a valley always occur in pairs.

9. Topographic maps published by the U.S. Geological Survey are contoured in feet or meters referenced to sea level.

Figure 11 Some general rules for contour lines.

plane from which elevations are measured for most topographic maps is mean (average) sea level. The datum for a map is usually indicated in the lower, central margin of the map with the phrase, "Datum is . . ."

Contour lines must conform to certain guidelines. Figure 11 presents some of the general rules that apply to contour lines.

The **contour interval** (CI) is the vertical difference in elevation between adjacent contour lines. All contour lines are multiples of the contour interval. For example, for a contour interval of 20 feet, the lines may read 420', 440', 460', etc. Most maps use the smallest contour interval possible to provide the greatest detail for the surface that is being mapped. The contour interval of a topographic map is usually indicated in the lower central margin of the map with the phrase, "Contour interval . . ." *The contour interval should always be known before using a topographic map.*

To help determine the elevation of the contour lines, on most topographic maps every fifth contour line, called an **index contour,** is printed as a bold line and the elevation of the line is indicated. Reference points of elevation, called **bench marks** (BM), are also often present on the map and can be used to establish elevations.

Contour lines that are close together indicate a steep **slope** (vertical change in elevation per horizontal distance, usually expressed in feet/mile or meters/kilometer), while widely spaced lines show a gradual slope. Consequently, the "shading" that results from closely spaced contour lines allows for the recognition of such features as hills, valleys, ridges, etc.

Relief is defined as the difference in elevation between two points on a map. *Total relief* is the difference between the highest and lowest points on a map. *Local relief* refers to the difference in elevation between two specified points, for example, a hill and nearby valley.

Examining Contour Lines

Figure 12 shows a contour map of volcanic cones, along with a stereoscopic contour map of the same fea-

tures. The large volcano illustrated is very similar to the one you observed in the stereogram, Figure 2.

30. Examine the stereoscopic contour map in Figure 12 by centering your stereoscope over the center line and observing the three-dimensional image. Before continuing the exercise, compare the stereoscopic image closely with the contour map. Examine the features noted in the caption on both maps, paying particular attention to the use of *hachure marks* on contours to show a depression.

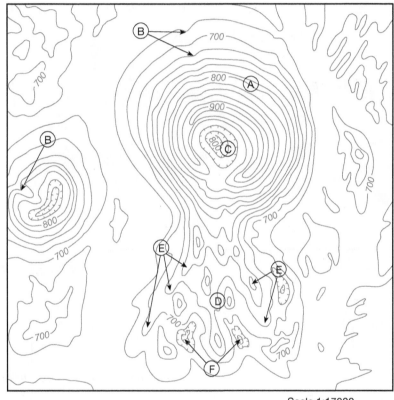

A. Contour Map

Scale 1:17000
Contour interval 20 feet

Figure 12 Contour map and stereoscopic contour map of the same volcanic cones. The two maps show a large, steep-sided cinder cone (**A**) with a well-developed crater (**C**) at its summit. Ridges (**E**) and depressions (**F**) are evident on the lava flows (**D**), while water erosion has carved gullies (**B**) on the sides of the cones. (From Horace MacMahan, Jr., *Stereogram Book of Contours*, p. 18. Copyright (c) 1972, Hubbard Scientific Company. Reprinted by permission of American Educational Products—Hubbard Scientific.)

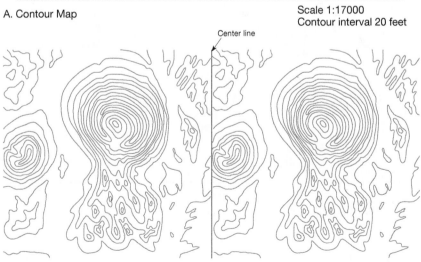

B. Stereoscopic Contour Map

Figure 13 shows both a perspective view and contour map of a hypothetical area situated along an ocean coast. The elevations in feet above mean sea level of several contour lines and points are identified on the map for reference. Use Figure 13 to answer questions 31–37.

31. What is the contour interval that has been used on the map?

    Contour interval: _____ feet

32. Indicate the two areas on the map that have the steepest slopes by writing the word "steep" on the map. What characteristic of the contour lines shows that the slopes are steep?

    _____

33. Notice what happens to the contour lines as they cross a stream. The "peak" formed by a contour line as it crosses a stream points (upstream, downstream). Circle your answer.

34. What are the elevations of the points designated with the following letters?

    Point A: _____ feet

    Point B: _____ feet

    Point C: _____ feet

35. The approximate elevation of the church is (12, 22, 32) feet. Circle your answer.

36. What is the total relief shown on the map?

    Highest elevation (_____ft) − lowest elevation (_____ft) = total relief (_____ft)

A. Perspective aerial view

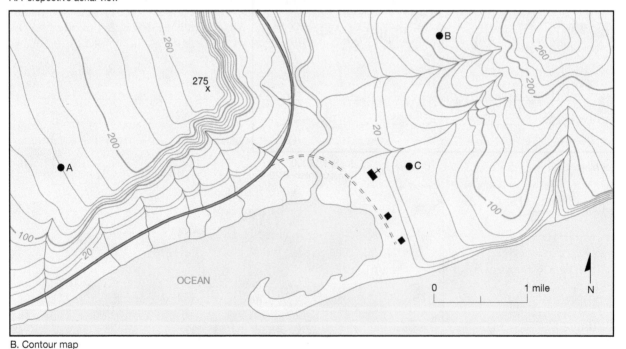

B. Contour map

Figure 13 Perspective (A) and map (B) view of a hypothetical coastal area. All elevations are in feet above mean sea level. (After U.S. Geological Survey)

114

37. What is the slope of the mountain located on the east side of the diagram from its summit, directly south to the ocean?

Slope = _____ feet/mile

Use the topographic map supplied by your instructor to answer questions 38–43. PLEASE DO NOT WRITE OR MARK ON THE MAPS.

38. What is the datum that has been used for determining the elevations on the map?

Datum: _____

39. What is the contour interval of the map?

Contour interval: _____ feet

40. What are the lowest and highest elevations found on the map?

Lowest elevation: _____ feet

Highest elevation: _____ feet

41. What is the elevation of the exact center of the map?

Elevation: _____ feet

42. Your instructor will supply you with the names of three features (school, church, etc.) located on the map. Write the elevation of each feature in the following spaces.

Feature name: _____

   Elevation: _____

Feature name: _____

   Elevation: _____

Feature name: _____

   Elevation: _____

43. After examining the contour lines, etc., write a brief description of the slope of the land represented by the map.

_____

_____

_____

Constructing a Contour Map

Originally, contour maps were constructed by first surveying an area and establishing the elevations of several points in the field. The surveyor then sketched contour lines on the map by estimating their location between the points of known elevation. Today, topographic maps are made from stereoscopic aerial photographs that are computer processed to determine elevations and contours.

44. To help understand the process of drawing a contour map, using a pencil, complete the contour map shown in Figure 14. The points illustrated are of known elevation. The 100-foot contour line has been drawn to provide a reference. Using a 20-foot contour interval, draw a contour line for each 20-foot change in elevation below and above 100 feet (e.g., 80 feet, 60 feet, 120 feet, etc.). You will have to estimate the elevations between the points. Label each of the lines with the proper elevation.

45. In Figure 14, in general, the land slopes toward the (north, south). Circle your answer.

46. After examining the contour lines and elevations in Figure 14, show the directions that the streams are flowing by drawing arrows on the map.

47. What is the average slope of the stream on the west side of the map you drew in Figure 14?

Slope = _____ feet/mile

Drawing a Topographic Profile

Topographic maps, like most other maps, depict Earth's surface viewed from above. Often a topographic profile or "side-view" will provide a more useful representation of the elevations and slopes of an area. To change an overhead, or map, view into a profile, follow the steps illustrated in Figure 15.

48. Use the horizontal line and vertical scale in Figure 16 to construct a west–east profile along the profile line indicated on the contour map you have drawn in Figure 14. Follow the guidelines for preparing a topographic profile in Figure 15.

Air Photos, Satellite Images, and Maps on the Internet

Apply the concepts from this exercise in an examination of the aerial/satellite photographs and topographic maps that are available for your area by completing the corresponding online activity on the *Applications & Investigations in Earth Science* website at http://prenhall.com/earthsciencelab

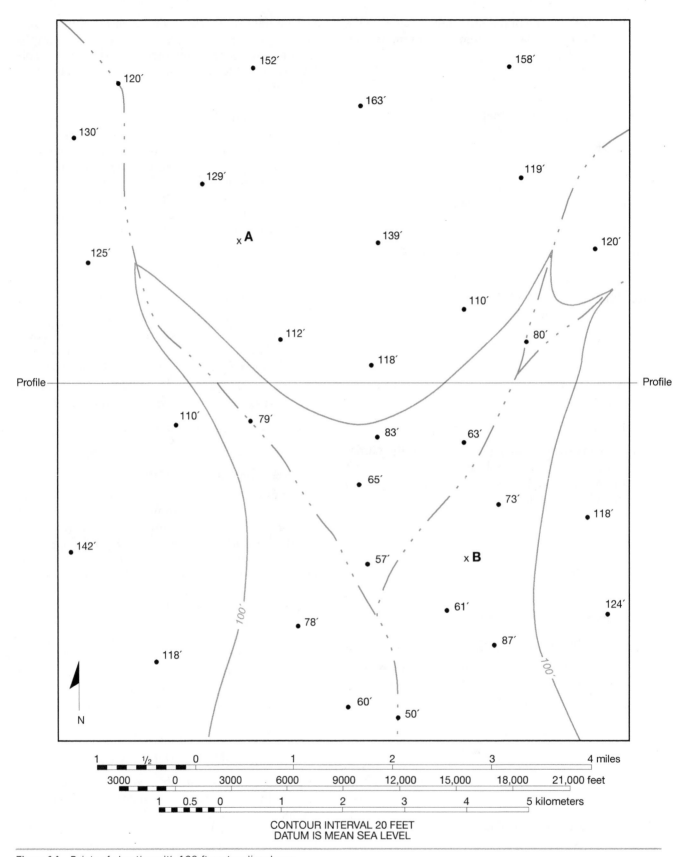

Figure 14 Points of elevation with 100-ft contour line drawn.

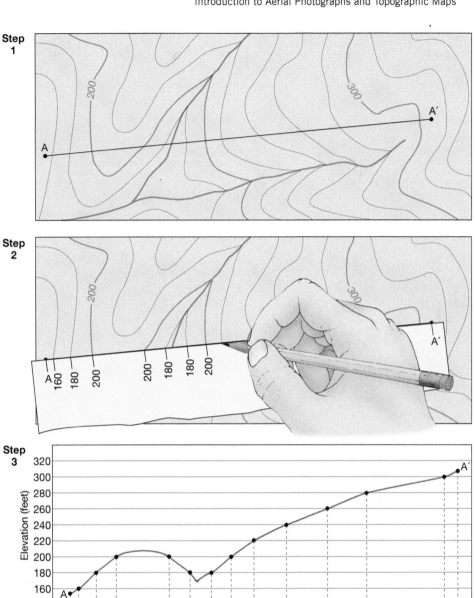

Figure 15 Construction of a topograph profile. **Step 1.** On the topographic map, draw a line along which the profile is to be constructed. Label the line A–A'.

As shown in **Step 2,** lay a piece of paper along line A–A'. Mark each place where a contour line intersects the edge of the paper and note the elevation of the contour line by each mark.

In **Step 3,** on a separate piece of paper, draw a horizontal line slightly longer than your profile line, A–A'. Select a vertical scale for your profile that begins slightly below the lowest elevation along the profile and extends slightly beyond the highest elevation. Mark this scale off on either side of the horizontal line. Lay the marked paper edge (from Step 2) along the horizontal line. Wherever you have marked a contour line on the edge of the paper, place a dot directly above the mark at an elevation on the vertical scale equal to that of the contour line. Connect the dots on the profile with a smooth line to see the finished product. (Note: Since you have more or less arbitrarily selected the vertical scale for the profile, *the finished profile may be somewhat vertically exaggerated and not the same as you would see it from the ground.*)

Marked paper with elevations recorded from **Step 2.**

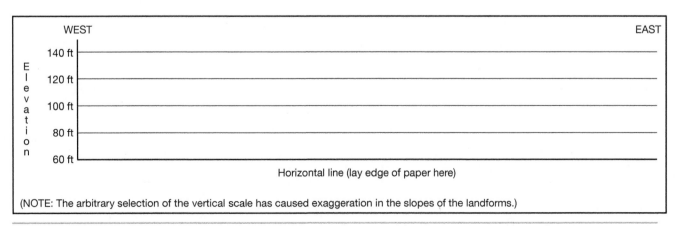

(NOTE: The arbitrary selection of the vertical scale has caused exaggeration in the slopes of the landforms.)

Figure 16 West–east topographic profile along the profile line on Figure 14.

Notes and calculations.

Introduction to Aerial Photographs and Topographic Maps

Date Due: _____

Name: _____

Date: _____

Class: _____

After you have finished this exercise, complete the following questions. You may have to refer to the exercise for assistance or to locate specific answers. Be prepared to submit this summary/report to your instructor at the designated time.

1. Use Figure 17, a portion of the Ontario, California, topographic map, to answer questions 1a.–1i.

a. One inch on the map is approximately _____ mile(s).

b. The fractional scale of the map is (1:12,000; 1:24,000; 1:62,500; 1:250,000). Circle your answer.

c. What is the direction and shortest distance a hiker would have to travel to reach the "Big

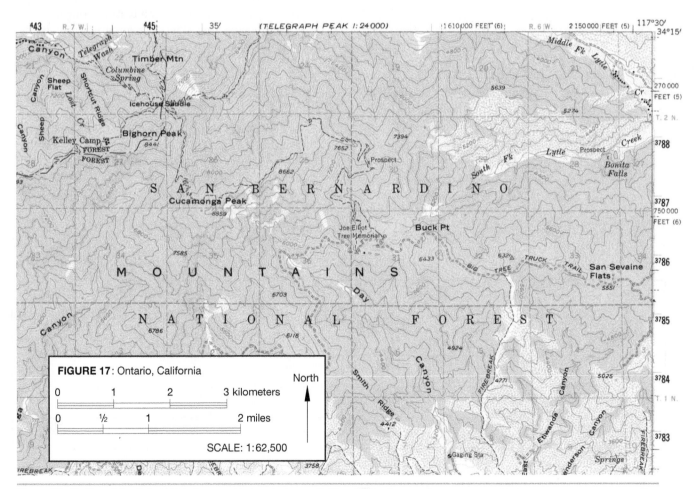

Figure 17 Portion of the Ontario, CA, topographic map to be used with question 1.

119

Tree Truck Trail" from Kelley Camp?

_____

_____

d. What is the approximate elevation of Kelley Camp?

_____

e. What is the contour interval of the map?

_____

f. Toward what direction does the stream in Day Canyon flow? How did you arrive at your answer?

_____

_____

g. Is the slope of the stream in Day Canyon steeper near Cucamonga Peak or the gaging station? How did you arrive at your answer?

_____

_____

h. Portions of which townships and ranges are covered by the map?

_____

i. Give the complete PLS location of Kelley Camp to the nearest $\frac{1}{4}$ of a $\frac{1}{4}$ section.

_____

2. What is the latitude and longitude to the nearest minute of the *exact center* of the topographic map supplied by your instructor?

Latitude: _____ Longitude: _____

3. The topographic map supplied by your instructor is a _____-minute series topographic map, which means that it:

_____

4. What are the numbers of the townships and ranges covered by the topographic map supplied by your instructor?

Townships: _____

Ranges: _____

5. Use the Public Land Survey system to give the name and location of a feature your instructor requested that you locate on your topographic map in question 29.

Name of feature: _____

Location:

_____ $\frac{1}{4}$, _____ $\frac{1}{4}$, Sec. _____, T _____, R _____

6. What was your calculated slope for the mountain in question 37?

Slope: _____ feet/mile

7. What was the elevation of a feature your instructor requested that you determine on your topographic map in question 42?

Feature name: _____

Elevation: _____

8. In Figure 18, sketch a copy of the west–east topographic profile you constructed in question 48. Label the appropriate elevations on the vertical axis of your sketch.

Figure 18   West–east topographic profile along the profile line on Figure 14.

Symbols used on topographic quadrangle maps produced by the U.S. Geological Survey
VARIATIONS WILL BE FOUND ON OLDER MAPS

Control data and monuments
Vertical control

Third order or better, with tablet	BM ×16.3
Third order or better, recoverable mark	× 120.0
Bench mark at found section corner	BM 18.6
Spot elevation	× 5.3

Contours
Topographic

Intermediate	
Index	
Supplementary	
Depression	
Cut; fill	

Bathymetric

Intermediate	
Index	
Primary	
Index primary	
Supplementary	

Boundaries

National	
State or territorial	
County or equivalent	
Civil township or equivalent	
Incorporated city or equivalent	
Park, reservation, or monument	

Surface features

Levee	Levee
Sand or mud area, dunes, or shifting sand	(Sand)
Intricate surface area	(Strip mine)
Gravel beach or glacial moraine	(Gravel)
Tailings pond	(Tailings pond)

Mines and caves

Quarry or open pit mine	
Gravel, sand, clay, or borrow pit	
Mine dump	(Mine dump)
Tailings	(Tailings)

Vegetation

Woods	
Scrub	
Orchard	
Vineyard	
Mangrove	(Mangrove)

Glaciers and permanent snowfields

Contours and limits	
Form lines	

Marine shoreline
Topographic maps

Approximate mean high water	
Indefinite or unsurveyed	

Topographic-bathymetric maps

Mean high water	
Apparent (edge of vegetation)	

Coastal features

Foreshore flat	
Rock or coral reef	
Rock bare or awash	
Group of rocks bare or awash	
Exposed wreck	
Depth curve; sounding	
Breakwater, pier, jetty, or wharf	
Seawall	

Rivers, lakes, and canals

Intermittent stream	
Intermittent river	
Disappearing stream	
Perennial stream	
Perennial river	
Small falls; small rapids	
Large falls; large rapids	
Masonry dam	
Dam with lock	
Dam carrying road	
Perennial lake; Intermittent lake or pond	
Dry lake	Dry lake
Narrow wash	
Wide wash	Wide wash
Canal, flume, or aquaduct with lock	
Well or spring; spring or seep	

Submerged areas and bogs

Marsh or swamp	
Submerged marsh or swamp	
Wooded marsh or swamp	
Submerged wooded marsh or swamp	
Rice field	(Rice)
Land subject to inundation	Max pool 431

Buildings and related features

Building	
School; church	
Built-up area	
Racetrack	
Airport	
Landing strip	
Well (other than water); windmill	
Tanks	
Covered reservoir	
Gaging station	
Landmark object (feature as labeled)	
Campground; picnic area	
Cemetery: small; large	Cem

Roads and related features
Roads on Provisional edition maps are not classified as primary, secondary, or light duty. They are all symbolized as light duty roads.

Primary highway	
Secondary highway	
Light duty road	
Unimproved road	
Trail	
Dual highway	
Dual highway with median strip	

Railroads and related features

Standard gauge single track; station	
Standard gauge multiple track	
Abandoned	

Transmission lines and pipelines

Power transmission line; pole; tower	
Telephone line	Telephone
Aboveground oil or gas pipeline	
Underground oil or gas pipeline	Pipeline

Location and Distance on Earth

The ability to find places and features on Earth's surface using maps and globes is an essential skill required of all Earth scientists. This exercise introduces the most commonly used system for determining location on Earth. Using the system as a foundation, you will examine ways to measure distance on Earth's surface.

Objectives

After you have completed this exercise, you should be able to:

1. Explain the most common system used for locating places and features on Earth.
2. Use Earth's grid system to accurately locate a place or feature.
3. Explain the relation between latitude and the angle of the North Star (Polaris) above the horizon.
4. Explain the relation between longitude and solar time.
5. Determine the shortest route and distance between any two places on Earth's surface.

Materials

ruler   calculator
protractor

Materials Supplied by Your Instructor

globe   50–80 cm length of
world wall map   string
atlas

Terms

Earth's grid	South Pole	solar time
latitude	longitude	standard time
parallel of	meridian of	great circle
latitude	longitude	small circle
equator	prime meridian	
North Pole	hemisphere	

Introduction

Globes and maps each have a system of north–south and east–west lines, called the **Earth's grid**, that forms the basis for locating points on Earth (Figure 1). The grid is, in effect, much like a large sheet of graph paper that has been laid over the surface of Earth. Using the system is very similar to using a graph; that is, the position of a point is determined by the intersection of two lines.

    Latitude is north–south distance on Earth (Figure 1). The lines (circles) of the grid that extend around Earth in an east–west direction are called **parallels of latitude**. *Parallels of latitude mark north and south distance from the equator on Earth's surface.* As their name implies, these circles are parallel to one another. Two places on Earth, the **North Pole** and **South Pole**, are exceptions; they are points of latitude rather than circles.

    Longitude is east–west distance on Earth (Figure 1). **Meridians of longitude** are each halves of circles that extend from the North Pole to the South Pole on

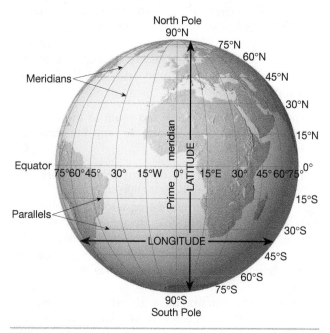

Figure 1 Earth's grid system.

one side of Earth. *Meridians of longitude mark east and west distance from the* **prime meridian** *on Earth's surface.* Adjacent meridians are farthest apart on the equator and converge (come together) toward the poles.

> **The intersection of a parallel of latitude with a meridian of longitude determines the location of a point on Earth's surface.**

Earth's shape is nearly spherical. Since parallels and meridians mark distances on a sphere, their designation, like distance around a circle, is given in *degrees* (°). For more precise location, a degree can be subdivided into sixty equal parts, called *minutes* ('), and a minute of angle can be divided into sixty parts, called *seconds* ("). Thus, 31°10'20" means 31 degrees, 10 minutes, and 20 seconds.

The type of map or globe used determines the accuracy to which a place may be located. On detailed maps it is often possible to estimate latitude and longitude to the nearest degree, minute, and second. On the other hand, when using a world map or globe, it may only be possible to estimate latitude and longitude to the nearest whole degree or two.

In addition to showing location on Earth, latitude and longitude can be used to determine distance. Knowing the shape and size of Earth, the distance in miles and kilometers covered by a degree of latitude or longitude has been calculated. These measurements provide the foundation for navigation.

Determining Latitude

The equator is a circle drawn on a globe that is equally distant from both the North Pole and South Pole. It divides the globe into two equal halves, called **hemispheres**. The equator serves as the beginning point for determining latitude and is assigned the value 0°00'00" latitude.

> **Latitude is distance north and south of the equator, measured as an angle in degrees from the center of Earth (Figure 2).**

Latitude begins at the equator, extends north to the North Pole, designated 90°00'00"N latitude (a 90° angle measured north from the equator), and also extends south to the South Pole, designated 90°00'00"S latitude. *The poles and all parallels of latitude, with the exception of the equator, are designated either N (if they are north of the equator) or S (if they are south of the equator).*

1. Locate the equator on a globe. Figure 3 represents Earth, with point B its center. Sketch and label the equator on the diagram in Figure 3. Also label the Northern Hemisphere and Southern Hemisphere on the diagram.

2. On Figure 3, make an angle by drawing a line from point A on the equator to point B (the center

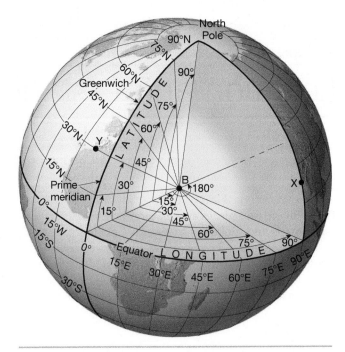

Figure 2 Measuring latitude and longitude. The angle measured from the equator to the center of Earth (B) and then northward to the parallel where point Y is located is 30°. Therefore, the latitude of point Y is 30°N. All points on the same parallel as Y are designated 30°N latitude.

The angle measured from the prime meridian where it crosses the equator to the center of Earth (B) and then eastward to the meridian where point X is located, is 90°. Therefore, the longitude of point X is 90°E. All points on the same meridian as X are designated 90°E longitude.

of Earth). Then extend the line from point B to point C in the Northern Hemisphere. The angle you have drawn (∠ABC) is 45°. Therefore, by definition of latitude, point C is at 45°N latitude.

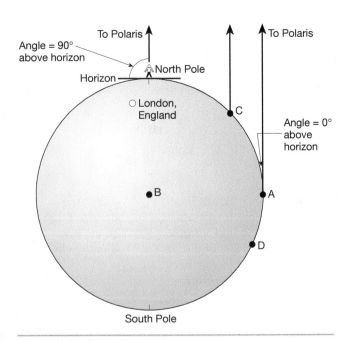

Figure 3 Hypothetical Earth.

3. Draw a line on Figure 3 parallel to the equator that also goes through point C. All points on this line are 45°N latitude.

4. Using a protractor, measure ∠ABD on Figure 3. Then draw a line parallel to the equator that also goes through point D. Label the line with its proper latitude.

On a map or globe, parallels may be drawn at any interval.

5. How many degrees of latitude separate the parallels on the globe you are using?

_____ degrees of latitude between each parallel

6. Keep in mind that the lines (circles) of latitude are parallel to the equator and to each other. Locate some other parallels on the globe. Sketch and label a few of these on Figure 3.

7. Use the diagram that illustrates parallels of latitude, Figure 4, to answer questions 7a and 7b.

   a. Accurately draw and label the following additional parallels of latitude on the figure.

   5°N latitude

   10°S latitude

   25°N latitude

   b. Refer to Figure 4. Write out the latitude for each designated point as was done for points A and B. Remember to indicate whether the point is north or south of the equator by writing an N or S and include the word "latitude."

   Point A: (30°N latitude)   Point D: _____

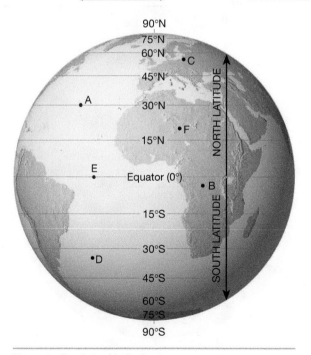

Figure 4   Parallels of latitude.

Point B: (5°S latitude)   Point E: _____

Point C: _____   Point F: _____

8. Use a globe or atlas to locate the cities listed below and give their latitude to the nearest degree. Indicate N or S and include the word "latitude."

   Moscow, Russia: _____

   Durban, South Africa: _____

   Your home city: _____

   Your college campus city: _____

9. By using a globe or atlas, give the name of a city or feature that is equally as far south of the equator as your home city is north.

   _____

10. The farthest one can be from the equator is (45, 90, 180) degrees of latitude. Circle your answer.

11. The two places on Earth that are farthest from the equator to the north and to the south are called the

   _____ and _____.

There are five special parallels of latitude marked and named on most globes.

12. Use a globe or atlas to locate the following special parallels and indicate the name given to each.

                                              NAME OF PARALLEL

   66°30'00"N latitude: _____

   23°30'00"N latitude: _____

   0°00'00" latitude: _____

   23°30'00"S latitude: _____

   66°30'00"S latitude: _____

Latitude and the North Star

Today most ships use GPS navigational satellites to determine their location. (For information about the Global Positioning System, visit the website listed at the end of this exercise.) However, early explorers were well aware of the concept of latitude and could use the angle of the North Star (a star named Polaris) above the horizon to determine their north–south position in the Northern Hemisphere. As shown on Figure 3, someone standing at the North Pole would look overhead (90° angle above the horizon) to see Polaris. Their latitude is 90°00'00"N. On the other hand, someone standing on the equator, 0°00'00" latitude, would observe Polaris on the horizon (0° angle above the horizon).

Use Figure 3 to answer questions 13–14.

13. The angle of Polaris above the horizon for someone standing at point C would be (45°, 90°, 180°). Circle your answer.

14. What is the relation between a particular latitude and the angle of Polaris above the horizon at that latitude?

_____

15. What is the angle of Polaris above the horizon at the following cities?

**ANGLE OF POLARIS
ABOVE THE HORIZON**

Fairbanks, AK: _____62°_____ degrees

St. Paul, MN: _____44°_____ degrees

New Orleans, LA: _____30°_____ degrees

Your home city: _____38°_____ degrees

Your college campus city: _____38°_____ degrees

Determining Longitude

Meridians are the north–south lines (half circles) on the globe that converge at the poles and are farthest apart along the equator. They are used to determine longitude, which is distance east and west on Earth (Figure 1). Each meridian extends from pole to pole on one side of the globe.

Notice on the globe that all meridians are alike. The choice of a zero, or beginning, meridian was arbitrary. The meridian that was chosen by international agreement in 1884 to be 0°00′00″ longitude passes through the Royal Astronomical Observatory at Greenwich, England, located near London. This internationally accepted reference for longitude is named the *prime meridian.*

Longitude is distance, measured as an angle in degrees **east and west of the prime meridian** (Figure 2).

Longitude begins at the prime meridian (0°00′00″ longitude) and extends to the east and to the west, halfway around Earth to the 180°00′00″ meridian, which is directly opposite the prime meridian. *All meridians, with the exception of the prime meridian and the 180° meridian, are designated either E (if they are east of the prime meridian) or W (if they are west of the prime meridian).*

16. Locate the prime meridian on a globe. Sketch and label it on the diagram of Earth, Figure 3.

17. Label the Eastern Hemisphere, that half of the globe with longitudes east of the prime meridian, and the Western Hemisphere on Figure 3.

On a map or globe, meridians can be drawn at any interval.

18. How many degrees of longitude separate each of the meridians on your globe?

_____ degrees of longitude between each meridian

19. Keep in mind that meridians are farthest apart at the equator and converge at the poles. Sketch and label several meridians on Figure 3.

20. Use the diagram that illustrates meridians of longitude, Figure 5, to answer questions 20a and 20b.

   a. Accurately draw and label the following additional meridians of longitude on the figure.

   35°W longitude

   70°E longitude

   10°W longitude

   b. Refer to Figure 5. Write out the longitude for each designated point as was done for points A and B. Remember to indicate whether the point is east or west of the prime meridian by writing an E or W and include the word "longitude."

   Point A: (30°E longitude) Point D: _____

   Point B: (20°W longitude) Point E: _____

   Point C: _____   Point F: _____

21. Use a globe or atlas to locate the cities listed below and give their longitude to the nearest degree. Indicate either E or W and include the word "longitude."

Wellington,   New   Zealand:
_____

Honolulu, Hawaii: _____

Your   home   city:

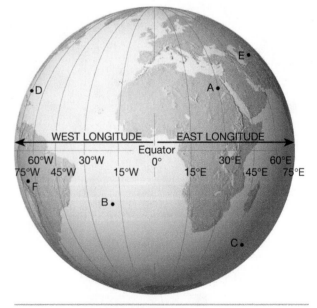

Figure 5 Meridians of longitude.

126

22. Using a globe or atlas, give the name of a city, feature, or country that is at the same latitude as your home city but equally distant from the prime meridian in the opposite hemisphere.

---

23. The farthest a place can be directly east or west of the prime meridian is (45, 90, 180) degrees of longitude. Circle your answer.

Longitude and Time

Time, while independent of latitude, is very much related to longitude. This fact allows for time to be used in navigation to accurately determine one's location. By knowing the difference in time between two places, one with known longitude, the longitude of the second place can be determined.

Time on Earth can be kept in two ways. **Solar**, or **Sun**, **time** uses the position of the Sun in the sky to determine time. **Standard time**, the system used throughout most of the world, divides the globe into 24 standard time zones. Everyone living within the same standard time zone keeps the clock set the same. Of the two, solar time is used to determine longitude.

The following basic facts are important to understanding time.

- Earth rotates on its axis from west to east (eastward) or counterclockwise when viewed from above the North Pole (Figure 6).

- It is noon, Sun time, on the meridian that is directly facing the Sun (the Sun has reached its highest position in the sky, called the *zenith*) and midnight on the meridian on the opposite side of Earth.

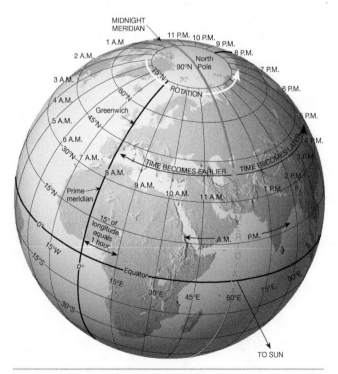

Figure 6 The noon meridian and solar time.

- The time interval from one noon by the Sun to the next noon averages 24 hours and is known as the *mean solar day*.

- Earth turns through 360° of longitude in one mean solar day, which is equivalent to 15° of longitude per hour or 1° of longitude every 4 minutes of time.

- Places that are east or west of each other, regardless of the distance, have different solar times. For example, people located to the east of the noon meridian have already experienced noon; their time is afternoon [P.M.—*post* (after) *meridiem* (the noon meridian)]. People living west of the noon meridian have yet to reach noon; their time is before noon [A.M.—*ante* (before) *meridiem* (the noon meridian)]. *Time becomes later going eastward and earlier going westward.*

Use the basic facts of time to answer questions 24–26.

24. What would be the solar time of a person living 1° of longitude west of the noon meridian? Be sure to indicate A.M. or P.M. with your answer.

Solar time: ___11:56___ (A.M., P.M.)

25. What would be the solar time of a person located 4° of longitude east of the noon meridian?

Solar time: ___12:16pm___ (A.M., P.M.)

26. If it is noon, solar time, at 70°W longitude, what is the solar time at each of the following locations?

	SOLAR TIME
72°W longitude:	11:58am
65°W longitude:	12:20pm
90°W longitude:	10:40am
110°E longitude:	4:0am

Early navigators had to wait for the invention of accurate clocks, called *chronometers*, before they could determine longitude. Today most navigation is done using satellites, but ships still carry chronometers as a backup system.

The shipboard chronometer is set to keep the time at a known place on Earth, for example, the prime meridian. If it is noon by the Sun where the ship is located, and at that same instant the chronometer indicates that it is 8 A.M. on the prime meridian, the ship must be 60° of longitude (4 hours difference × 15° per hour) east (the ship's time is later) of the prime meridian (Figure 6). The difference in time need not be in whole hours. Thirty minutes difference in time between two places would be equivalent to 7.5° of longitude, twenty minutes would equal 5°, and so forth.

27. It is exactly noon by the Sun at a ship's location. What is the ship's longitude if, at that instant, the time on the prime meridian is the following? (*Note:* Drawing a diagram showing the prime meridian, the ship's location east or west of the prime meridian, and the difference in hours may be helpful.)

6:00 P.M.: _____

1:00 A.M.: _____

2:30 P.M.: _____

Using Earth's Grid System

Using both parallels of latitude and meridians of longitude, you can accurately locate any point on the surface of Earth.

28. Using Figure 7, determine the latitude and longitude of each of the lettered points and write your answers in the following spaces. As a guide, Point A has already been done. Remember to indicate whether the point is N or S latitude and E or W longitude. The only exceptions are the equator, prime meridian, and 180° meridian. They are given no direction because each is a single line and cannot be confused with any other line. Convention dictates that latitude is always listed first.

Point A: (30°N) latitude,   (60°E) longitude

Point B: _30 S_ latitude,   _30W_ longitude

Point C: _0_ latitude,   _90W_ longitude

Point D: _45N_ latitude,   _75W_ longitude

Point E: _12N_ latitude,   _20W_ longitude

29. Locate the following points on Figure 7. Place a dot on the figure at the proper location and label each point with the designated letter.

Point F: 15°S latitude, 75°W longitude

Point G: 45°N latitude, 0° longitude

Point H: 30°S latitude, 60°E longitude

Point I: 0° latitude, 30°E longitude

30. Use a globe, map, or atlas to determine the latitude and longitude of the following cities.

Kansas City, MO: _____

Miami, FL: _____

Oslo, Norway: _____

Auckland, New Zealand: _____

Quito, Ecuador: _____

Baghdad, Iraq: _____

31. Beginning with a globe or world wall map, and then proceeding to an atlas, determine the city or feature at the following locations.

19°28′N latitude, 99°09′W longitude:

_____

41°52′N latitude, 12°37′E longitude:

_____

1°30′S latitude, 33°00′E longitude:

_____

When you study the Earth sciences, it is important to be familiar with the major physical features of Earth's surface. Identifying the features on a map will help acquaint you with their location for future reference.

32. Use a wall map of the world or world map in an atlas to find the following water bodies, rivers, and mountains. Examine their latitudes and longitudes, and then label each on the world map, Figure 8. To conserve space, mark only the num-

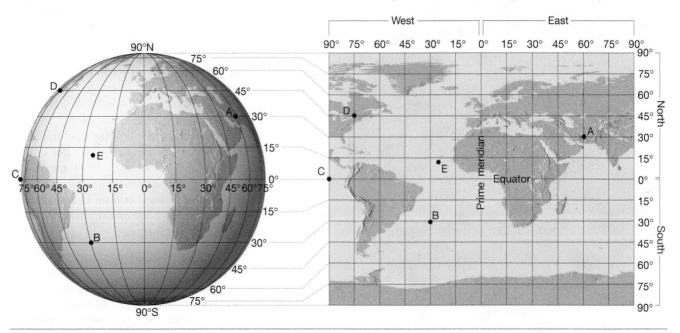

Figure 7   Locating places using Earth's grid system.

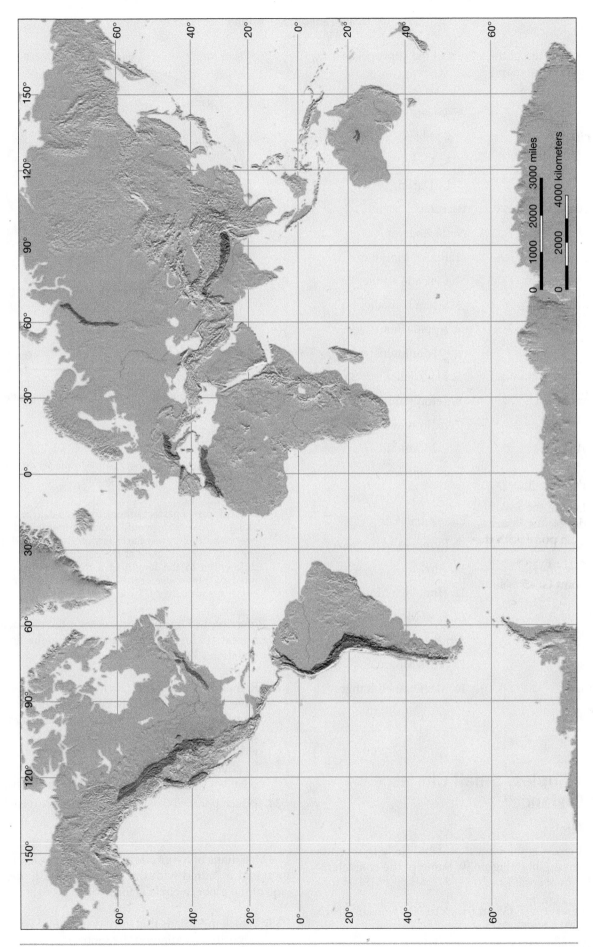

Figure 8   Generalized world map showing select physical features.

ber or letter of the feature at the appropriate location on the map.

Water Bodies

A. Pacific Ocean

B. Atlantic Ocean

C. Indian Ocean

D. Arctic Ocean

E. Gulf of Mexico

F. Mediterranean Sea

G. Caribbean Sea

H. Persian Gulf

I. Red Sea

J. Sea of Japan

K. Black Sea

L. Caspian Sea

Rivers

North America

a. Mississippi

b. Colorado

c. Missouri

d. Ohio

South America

e. Amazon

Europe and Asia

f. Volga

g. Mekong

h. Ganges

i. Yangtze

Africa and Australia

j. Nile

k. Congo

l. Darling

Mountains

North America

1. Rocky Mountains

2. Cascade Range

3. Sierra Nevada

4. Appalachian
      Mountains

5. Black Hills

6. Teton Range

7. Adirondack
      Mountains

South America

8. Andes Mountains

Europe and Asia

9. Pyrenees Mountains

10. Alps

11. Himalaya Mountains

12. Ural Mountains

Africa and Australia

13. Atlas Mountains

14. MacDonnell Ranges

Great Circles, Small Circles, and Distance

Great Circles

A **great circle** is the largest possible circle that can be drawn on a globe (Figure 9). Some of the characteristics of a great circle are

- A great circle divides the globe into two equal parts, called *hemispheres.*

- An infinite number of great circles can be drawn on a globe. Therefore, a great circle can be drawn that passes through any two places on Earth's surface.

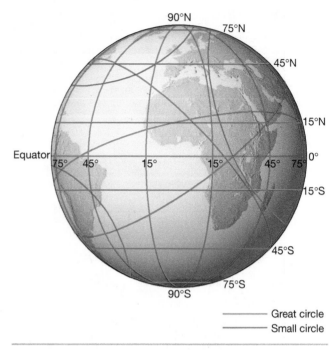

Figure 9 Illustrated are a few of the infinite number of great circles and small circles that can be drawn on the globe.

- The shortest distance between two places on Earth is along the great circle that passes through those two places.

- If Earth were a perfect sphere, then one degree of angle along a great circle would cover an identical distance everywhere. Because Earth is slightly flattened at the *poles and bulges slightly* at the equator, there are small differences in the length of a degree. However, for most purposes, *one degree of angle along a great circle equals approximately 111 kilometers or 69 miles.*

Referring to Figure 9 and keeping the characteristics of great circles in mind, examine a globe and answer questions 33–35.

33. Remember that great circles do not necessarily have to follow parallels or meridians. Estimate several great circles on the globe. Do this by wrapping a piece of string around the globe that divides the globe into two equal halves. You should be able to see that there are an infinite number of great circles that can be marked on the globe.

34. Which parallel(s) of latitude is/are a great circle(s)?

_____

Meridians of longitude are each half circles. If each meridian is paired with the meridian on the opposite side of the globe, a circle is formed.

35. Which meridians that have been paired with their opposite meridian on the globe are great circles?

_____

Small Circles

Any circle on the globe that does not meet the characteristics of a great circle is considered a **small circle** (Figure 9). Therefore, a small circle *does not* divide the globe into two equal parts and *is not* the shortest distance between two places on Earth. Referring to Figure 9 and keeping the characteristics of small circles in mind, examine a globe and answer questions 36–38.

36. In general, which parallels of latitude are small circles?

_____

37. Which two latitudes are actually points, rather than circles?

_____

38. In general, which meridians that have been paired with their opposite meridian on the globe are small circles?

_____

39. Indicate, by placing an "X" in the appropriate column, which of the following pairs of points illustrated on the Earth's grid in Figure 7 are on a great circle and which are on a small circle.

	GREAT CIRCLE	SMALL CIRCLE
Points A–H	_____	_____
Points D–G	_____	_____
Points C–I	_____	_____
Points B–H	_____	_____

40. Now that you know the characteristics of great and small circles, complete the following statements by circling the correct response.

   a. All meridians are halves of (great, small) circles.

   b. With the exception of the equator, all parallels are (great, small) circles.

   c. The equator is a (great, small) circle.

   d. The poles are (points, lines) of latitude, rather than circles.

Determining Distance Along a Great Circle

Determining the distance between two places on Earth when both are on the equator or the same great circle meridian requires two steps:

Step 1: Determine the number of degrees along the great circle between the two places (degrees of longitude on the equator or degrees of latitude on a meridian).

Step 2: Multiply the number of degrees by 111 kilometers or 69 miles (the approximate number of kilometers or miles per degree for any great circle).

Use a globe and these steps to answer questions 41 and 42.

41. Approximately how many miles would you journey if you traveled from 10°W longitude to 40°E longitude at the equator by way of the shortest route?

_____ miles

42. Approximately how many kilometers is London, England, directly north of the equator?

_____ kilometers

Determining the shortest distance between two places on Earth that are *not* both on the equator or the same great circle meridian requires the four steps (Figure 10):

Step 1: On a globe, determine the great circle that intersects both places.

Step 2: Stretch a piece of string along the great circle between the two places on the globe and mark the distance between them on the string with your fingers (Figure 10A).

Step 3: While still marking the distance with your fingers, place the string on the equator with one end on the prime meridian. Determine the number of degrees along the great circle between the two places by measuring the marked string's length in degrees of longitude along the equator, which is also a great circle (Figure 10B).

Step 4: Multiply the number of degrees along the great circle by 69 miles (111 kilometers) to arrive at the approximate distance. (For example, the great circle distance between X and Y in Figure 10 would be approximately 2,070 miles, 30° × 69 miles/degree, or 3330 kilometers, 30° × 111 kilometers/degree.)

Use a globe, a piece of string, and the four steps to answer questions 43 and 44.

43. Determine the approximate great circle distance in degrees, miles, and kilometers from Memphis, Tennessee, to Tokyo, Japan.

Degrees along the great circle between Memphis and Tokyo = _____°

Distance along the great circle between Memphis and Tokyo = _____ miles (_____ km)

131

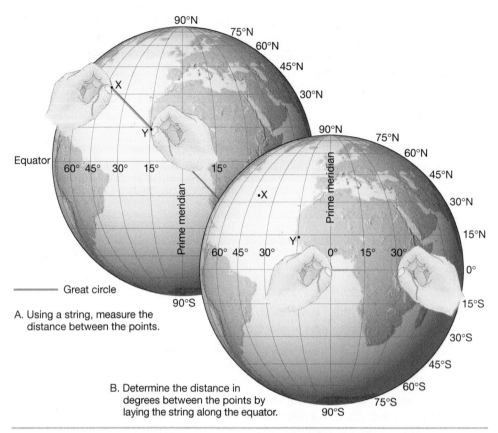

A. Using a string, measure the distance between the points.

B. Determine the distance in degrees between the points by laying the string along the equator.

Figure 10 Determining the distance between two places on Earth along a great circle other than the equator or great circle meridian. In the example illustrated, the distance between X and Y along the great circle is 30°, which is approximately equivalent to 2,070 miles (3,330 kilometers).

44. Describe the flight route, by listing states, countries, etc., that a plane would follow as it flew by way of the shortest route between Memphis, Tennessee, and Tokyo, Japan.

_____

_____

Determining Distance Along a Parallel

Since all parallels except the equator are small circles, the length of one degree of longitude along a parallel, other than the equator, will always be less than 69 miles or 111 kilometers. Table 1 shows the length of a degree of longitude at various latitudes on Earth.

45. Examine a globe. What do you observe about the distance around Earth along each parallel as you get farther away from the equator?

_____

46. Use Table 1, "Longitude as distance," to determine the length of one degree of longitude at each of the following parallels.

LENGTH OF 1° OF LONGITUDE

15° latitude: _____ km, _____ miles

30° latitude: _____ km, _____ miles

45° latitude: _____ km, _____ miles

80° latitude: _____ km, _____ miles

47. Use the Earth's grid illustrated in Figure 7 to determine the distances between the following points.

Distance between points D and G:

_____ degrees × _____ miles/degree

= _____ miles

Distance between points B and H:

_____ degrees × _____ km/degree

= _____ km

Memphis, Tennessee, and Tokyo, Japan, are both located at about 35°N latitude.

48. Use a globe or world map to determine how many degrees of longitude separate Memphis, Tennessee, from Tokyo, Japan.

Table 1 **Longitude as Distance**

°Lat.	Length of 1° Long. km	Length of 1° Long. miles	°Lat.	Length of 1° Long. km	Length of 1° Long. miles	°Lat.	Length of 1° Long. km	Length of 1° Long. miles
0	111.367	69.172	30	96.528	59.955	60	55.825	34.674
1	111.349	69.161	31	95.545	59.345	61	54.131	33.622
2	111.298	69.129	32	94.533	58.716	62	52.422	32.560
3	111.214	69.077	33	93.493	58.070	63	50.696	31.488
4	111.096	69.004	34	92.425	57.407	64	48.954	30.406
5	110.945	68.910	35	91.327	56.725	65	47.196	29.314
6	110.760	68.795	36	90.203	56.027	66	45.426	28.215
7	110.543	68.660	37	89.051	55.311	67	43.639	27.105
8	110.290	68.503	38	87.871	54.578	68	41.841	25.988
9	110.003	68.325	39	86.665	53.829	69	40.028	24.862
10	109.686	68.128	40	85.431	53.063	70	38.204	23.729
11	109.333	67.909	41	84.171	52.280	71	36.368	22.589
12	108.949	67.670	42	82.886	51.482	72	34.520	21.441
13	108.530	67.410	43	81.575	50.668	73	32.662	20.287
14	108.079	67.130	44	80.241	49.839	74	30.793	19.126
15	107.596	66.830	45	78.880	48.994	75	28.914	17.959
16	107.079	66.509	46	77.497	48.135	76	27.029	16.788
17	106.530	66.168	47	76.089	47.260	77	25.134	15.611
18	105.949	65.807	48	74.659	46.372	78	23.229	14.428
19	105.337	65.427	49	73.203	45.468	79	21.320	13.242
20	104.692	65.026	50	71.727	44.551	80	19.402	12.051
21	104.014	64.605	51	70.228	43.620	81	17.480	10.857
22	103.306	64.165	52	68.708	42.676	82	15.551	9.659
23	102.565	63.705	53	67.168	41.719	83	13.617	8.458
24	101.795	63.227	54	65.604	40.748	84	11.681	7.255
25	100.994	62.729	55	64.022	39.765	85	9.739	6.049
26	100.160	62.211	56	62.420	38.770	86	7.796	4.842
27	99.297	61.675	57	60.798	37.763	87	5.849	3.633
28	98.405	61.121	58	59.159	36.745	88	3.899	2.422
29	97.481	60.547	59	57.501	35.715	89	1.950	1.211
30	96.528	59.955	60	55.825	34.674	90	0.000	0.000

_____ degrees of longitude separate Memphis, Tennessee, and Tokyo, Japan.

49. From the longitude as distance table, Table 1, the length of one degree of longitude at latitude 35°N is

_____ km (_____ miles).

50. How many miles is Tokyo, Japan, *directly* west of Memphis, TN? Show your calculation below.

_____ miles

51. In question 43 you determined the great circle distance between Memphis, Tennessee, and Tokyo, Japan. How many miles shorter is the great circle route between these cities than the east–west distance along a parallel (question 50)?

The great circle route is _____ miles shorter.

Location and Distance on Earth on the Internet

Continue your analyses of the topics presented in this exercise by completing the corresponding online activity on the *Applications & Investigations in Earth Science* website at http://prenhall.com/earthsciencelab

Notes and calculations.

Location and Distance on Earth

Date Due: _____

Name: _____

Date: _____

Class: _____

After you have finished this exercise, complete the following questions. You may have to refer to the exercise for assistance or to locate specific answers. Be prepared to submit this summary/report to your instructor at the designated time.

1. In Figure 11, prepare a diagram illustrating Earth's grid system. Include and label the equator and prime meridian. Refer to the diagram to explain the system used for locating points on the surface of Earth.

Figure 11   Diagram of Earth's grid system.

Explanation: _____

_____

_____

2. Define the following terms.

Parallel of latitude: _____

_____

Meridian of longitude: _____

_____

Great circle: _____

_____

3. Determine whether or not the following statements are true or false. If the statement is false, correct the word(s) so that it reads as a true statement.

T F a. The distance measured north or south of the prime meridian is called latitude.

T F b. All meridians, when paired with their opposite meridian on Earth, form great circles.

T F c. The equator is the only meridian that is a great circle.

4. What is the relation between the latitude of a place in the Northern Hemisphere and the angle of Polaris above the horizon at that place?

_____

5. Approximately how many miles does one degree equal along a great circle?

One degree along a great circle equals _____ miles.

6. What is the latitude and longitude of your home city?

_____ latitude, _____ longitude

7. Use a globe or map to determine, as accurately as possible, the latitude and longitude of Athens, Greece.

_____ latitude, _____ longitude

8. Write a brief paragraph describing how to determine the shortest distance between two places on Earth's surface.

_____

_____

_____

135

9. From question 51 of the exercise, how many miles shorter is the great circle route between Memphis, Tennessee, and Tokyo, Japan, than the straight east–west distance along a parallel?

_____ miles shorter

10. Approximately how many miles is it from London, England, to the South Pole? (Show your calculation.)

_____ miles

11. Using Figure 12, determine the latitude and longitude of each of the lettered points and write your answers in the following spaces.

Point A: _____

Point B: _____

Point C: _____

Point D: _____

Point E: _____

12. You are shipwrecked and floating in the Atlantic Ocean somewhere between London, England, and New York, New York. Fortunately, you managed to save your globe. You have been in London so your watch is still set for London time. It is noon, by the Sun, at your location. Your watch indicates that it is 4 P.M. in London. Are you closer to the United States or to England? Explain how you arrived at your answer.

_____

_____

_____

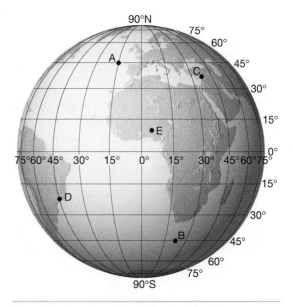

Figure 12 Locating places using Earth's grid.

Earth–Sun Relations

To life on this planet, the relations between Earth and the Sun are perhaps the most important of all astronomical phenomena. The variations in solar energy striking Earth as it rotates and revolves around the Sun cause the seasons and therefore are an appropriate starting point for studying weather and climate.

In this exercise you will investigate the reasons why the amount of solar radiation intercepted by Earth varies for different latitudes and changes throughout the year at a particular place (Figure 1).

Objectives

After you have completed this exercise, you should be able to:

1. Describe the effect that Sun angle has on the amount of solar radiation a place receives.
2. Explain why the intensity and duration of solar radiation varies with latitude.
3. Explain why the intensity and duration of solar radiation varies at any one place throughout the year.
4. Describe the significance of these special parallels of latitude: Tropic of Cancer, Tropic of Capricorn, Arctic Circle, Antarctic Circle, and equator.
5. Diagram the relation between Earth and the Sun on the dates of the solstices and equinoxes.
6. Determine the latitude where the overhead Sun is located on any day of the year.
7. Calculate the noon Sun angle for any place on Earth on any day.
8. Calculate the latitude of a place using the noon Sun angle.

Materials

metric ruler   colored pencils
protractor   calculator

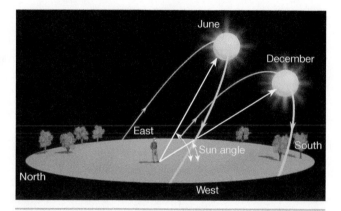

Figure 1   Daily paths of the Sun for June and December for an observer in the middle latitudes in the Northern Hemisphere. Notice that the angle of the Sun above the horizon is much greater in the summer than in the winter.

Materials Supplied by Your Instructor

globe
large rubber band or string

Terms

weather	solar constant	solstice
weather element	equator	equinox
weather control	Tropic of Cancer	analemma
solar intensity	Tropic of Capricorn	noon Sun
solar duration	Arctic Circle	angle
langley	Antarctic Circle	
calorie		

Introduction

Weather is the state of the atmosphere at a particular place for a short period of time. The condition of the atmosphere at any location and time is described by measuring the four basic **elements** of weather: temperature, moisture, air pressure, and wind. Of all the **controls** that are responsible for causing variations in the weather elements, the amount of solar radiation received at any location is the most important.

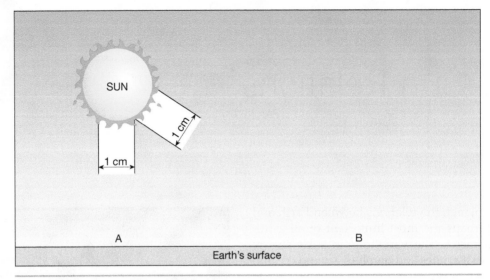

Figure 2 Vertical and oblique Sun beams.

Solar Radiation and the Seasons

The amount of solar energy (radiation) striking the outer edge of the atmosphere is not uniform over the face of Earth at any one time, nor is it constant throughout the year at any particular place. Rather, solar radiation at any location and time is determined by the Sun's **intensity** and **duration**. Intensity is the angle at which the rays of sunlight strike a surface, whereas duration refers to the length of daylight.

The standard unit of solar radiation is the **langley**, equal to one **calorie**[1] per square centimeter. The **solar constant**, or average intensity of solar radiation falling on a surface perpendicular to the solar beam at the outer edge of the atmosphere, is about 2 langleys per minute. As the radiation passes through the atmosphere, it undergoes absorption, reflection, and scattering. Therefore, at any one location, less radiation reaches Earth's surface than was originally intercepted at the upper atmosphere.

Solar Radiation and Latitude

The amount of radiation striking a square meter at the outer edge of the atmosphere, and eventually Earth's surface, varies with latitude because of a changing Sun angle (see Figure 1). To illustrate this fact, answer questions 1–11 using the appropriate figure.

1. On Figure Table 2, extend the 1-cm-wide beam of sunlight from the Sun vertically to point A on the

surface. Extend the second 1-cm-wide beam, beginning at the Sun, to the surface at point B.

Notice in Figure 2 that the Sun is directly overhead (vertical) at point A and the beam of sunlight strikes the surface at a 90° angle above the horizon.

Using Figure 2, answer questions 2–5.

2. Using a protractor, measure the angle between the surface and the beam of sunlight coming from the Sun to point B.

    _____° = angle of the Sun above the surface (horizon) at point B.

3. What are the lengths of the line segments on the surface covered by the Sun beam at point A and point B?

    Point A: _____ mm   point B: _____ mm

4. Of the two beams, beam (A, B) is more spread out at the surface and covers a larger area. Circle your answer.

5. More langleys per minute would be received by a square centimeter on the surface at point (A, B). Circle your answer.

Use Figure 3 to answer questions 6–11 concerning the total amount of solar radiation intercepted by each 30° segment of latitude on Earth.

6. With a metric ruler, measure the total width of incoming rays from point x to point y in Figure 3. The total width is _____ centimeters (_____ millimeters). Fill in your answers.

7. Assume the total width of the incoming rays from point x to point y equals 100% of the solar radiation that is intercepted by Earth. Each cen-

[1]The most familiar energy unit used to measure heat is the calorie, which is the quantity of heat energy needed to raise the temperature of one gram of water one degree Celsius. Do not confuse it with the so-called large Calorie (note the capital C), the kind counted by weight watchers. A Calorie is the amount of heat energy needed to raise the temperature of a kilogram (1,000 grams) of water 1 degree Celsius.

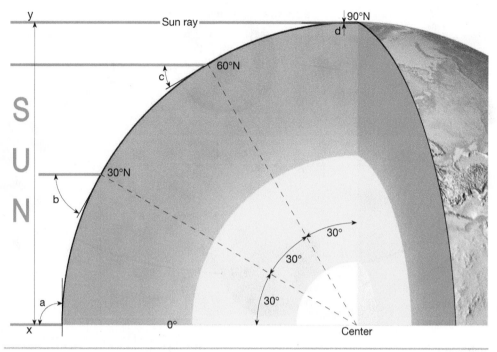

Figure 3 Distribution of solar radiation per 30° segment of latitude on Earth.

timeter would equal _____%, and each millimeter would equal _____%. Fill in your answers.

8. What percentage of the total incoming radiation is concentrated in each of the following zones?

    0°–30° = _____ mm = _____ %

    30°–60° = _____ mm = _____ %

    60°–90° = _____ mm = _____ %

9. Use a protractor to measure the angle between the surface and Sun ray at each of the following locations. (Angle b is already done as an example.)

    Angle a: _____ °   angle c: _____ °

    Angle b: ___60°___   angle d: _____ °

10. What is the general relation between the amount of radiation received in each 30° segment and the angle of the Sun's rays?

    _____

    _____

11. Explain in your own words what fact about Earth creates the unequal distribution of solar energy, even though each zone represents an equal 30° segment of latitude.

    _____

    _____

    _____

Yearly Variation in Solar Energy

The amount of solar radiation received at a particular place would remain constant throughout the year if it were not for these facts:

- Earth rotates on its axis and revolves around the Sun.
- The axis of Earth is inclined 23.5° from the perpendicular to the plane of its orbit.
- Throughout the year, the axis of Earth points to the same place in the sky, which causes the overhead (vertical or 90°) noon Sun to cross over the **equator** twice as it migrates from the **Tropic of Cancer** (23.5°N latitude) to the **Tropic of Capricorn** (23.5°S latitude) and back to the Tropic of Cancer.

As a consequence, the position of the vertical or overhead noon Sun shifts between the hemispheres, causing variations in the intensity of solar radiation and changes in the length of daylight and darkness. *The seasons are the result of this changing intensity and duration of solar energy and subsequent heating of the atmosphere.*

To help understand how the intensity and duration of solar radiation varies throughout the year, answer questions 12–31 after you have examined the location of the Tropic of Cancer, Tropic of Capricorn, **Arctic Circle**, and **Antarctic Circle** on a globe or world map.

12. List some of the countries each of the following special parallels of latitude passes through.

    Tropic of Cancer:_____

    Tropic of Capricorn: _____

    Arctic Circle: _____

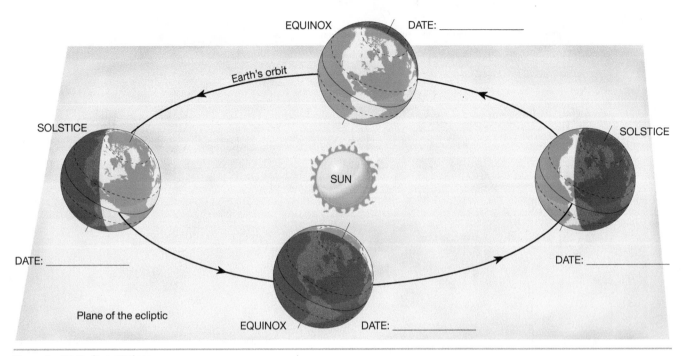

Figure 4 Earth–Sun relations.

13. Write the date represented by each position of Earth at the appropriate place in Figure 4. Then label the following on Earth at an equinox AND a solstice position.

North Pole and South Pole

Axis of Earth

Equator, Tropic of Cancer, Tropic of Capricorn

Arctic Circle and Antarctic Circle

Circle of illumination (day–night line)

Questions 14–19 refer to the June **solstice** position of Earth in Figure 4.

14. What term is used to describe the June 21–22 date in each hemisphere?

Northern Hemisphere: _____ solstice

Southern Hemisphere: _____ solstice

15. On June 21–22 the Sun's rays are perpendicular to Earth's surface at noon at the (Tropic of Cancer, equator, Tropic of Capricorn). Circle your answer.

16. What latitude is receiving the most intense solar energy on June 21–22?

Latitude: _____

17. Toward what direction, north or south, would you look to see the Sun at noon on June 21–22 if you lived at the following latitudes?

40°N latitude: _____

10°N latitude: _____

18. Position a rubber band, string, or pieces of tape on a globe corresponding to the *circle of illumination* on June 21–22. Then determine the approximate length of daylight at the following latitudes by examining the proportionate number of degrees of longitude a place located at each latitude spends in daylight as Earth rotates. (*Note:* Earth rotates a total of 360° of longitude per day. Therefore, each 15° of longitude is equivalent to one hour.)

70°N latitude: _____ hrs _____ min

40°S latitude: _____ hrs _____ min

40°N latitude: _____ hrs _____ min

90°S latitude: _____ hrs _____ min

0° latitude: _____ hrs _____ min

19. On June 21–22, latitudes north of the Arctic Circle are receiving (6, 12, 24) hours of daylight, while latitudes south of the Antarctic Circle are experiencing (6, 12, 24) hours of darkness. Circle your answers.

Questions 20–24 refer to the December solstice position of Earth in Figure 4.

20. What name is used to describe the December 21–22 date in each hemisphere?

Northern Hemisphere: _____ solstice

Southern Hemisphere: _____ solstice

21. On December 21–22 the Sun's rays are perpendicular to Earth's surface at noon on the (Tropic of

Table 1   Length of Daylight

LATITUDE (DEGREES)	SUMMER SOLSTICE	WINTER SOLSTICE	EQUINOXES
0	12 h	12 h	12 h
10	12 h 35 min	11 h 25 min	12
20	13 12	10 48	12
30	13 56	10 04	12
40	14 52	9 08	12
50	16 18	7 42	12
60	18 27	5 33	12
66.5	24 h	0 00	12
70	24 h (for 2 mo)	0 00	12
80	24 h (for 4 mo)	0 00	12
90	24 h (for 6 mo)	0 00	12

Cancer, equator, Tropic of Capricorn). Circle your answer.

22. On December 21–22 the (Northern, Southern) Hemisphere is receiving the most intense solar energy. Circle your answer.

23. If you lived at the equator, on December 21–22 you would look (north, south) to see the Sun at noon.

24. Refer to Table 1, "Length of daylight." What is the length of daylight at each of the following latitudes on December 21–22?

   90°N latitude: _____ hrs _____ min

   40°S latitude: _____ hrs _____ min

   40°N latitude: _____ hrs _____ min

   90°S latitude: _____ hrs _____ min

   0° latitude: _____ hrs _____ min

Questions 25–31 refer to the March and September **equinox** positions of Earth in Figure 4.

25. For those living in the Northern Hemisphere, what terms are used to describe the following dates?

   March 21: _____ equinox

   September 22: _____ equinox

26. For those living in the Southern Hemisphere, what terms are used to describe the following dates?

   March 21: _____ equinox

   September 22: _____ equinox

27. On March 21 and September 22 the Sun's rays are perpendicular to Earth's surface at noon at the (Tropic of Cancer, equator, Tropic of Capricorn). Circle your answer.

28. What latitude is receiving the most intense solar energy on March 21 and September 22?

   Latitude: _____

29. If you lived at 20°S latitude, you would look (north, south) to see the Sun at noon on March 21 and September 22. Circle your answer.

30. What is the relation between the North and South Poles and the circle of illumination on March 21 and September 22?

   _____

31. Write a brief statement describing the length of daylight everywhere on Earth on March 21 and September 22.

   _____

As you have seen, the latitude where the noon Sun is directly overhead (vertical, or 90° above the horizon) is easily determined for the solstices and equinoxes.

Figure 5 is a graph, called an **analemma**, that can be used to determine the latitude where the overhead noon Sun is located for any date. To determine the lat-

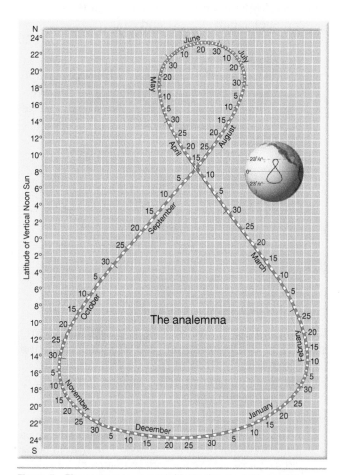

Figure 5   The analemma, a graph illustrating the latitude of the overhead (vertical) noon Sun throughout the year.

itude of the overhead noon Sun from the analemma, find the desired date on the graph and read the coinciding latitude along the left axis. Don't forget to indicate North or South when writing latitude.

32. Using a colored pencil, draw lines on Figure 5 that correspond to the equator, Tropic of Cancer, and Tropic of Capricorn. Label each of these special parallels of latitude on the figure.

33. Using the analemma, Figure 5, determine where the Sun is overhead at noon on the following dates.

    December 10: _____

    March 21: _____

    May 5: _____

    June 22: _____

    August 10: _____

    October 15: _____

34. The position of the overhead noon Sun is always located on or between which two parallels of latitude?

    _____°N (named the Tropic of _____) and

    _____°S (named the Tropic of _____)

35. The overhead noon Sun is located at the equator on September _____ and March _____. Together, these two days are called the _____. Fill in your answers.

36. Refer to Figure 5 and write a brief paragraph summarizing the yearly movement of the overhead noon Sun and how the intensity and duration of solar radiation varies over Earth's surface throughout the year.

    _____

    _____

    _____

    _____

Calculating Noon Sun Angle

Knowing where the noon Sun is overhead on any given date (the analemma), you can determine the angle above the horizon of the noon Sun at any other latitude on that same day. The relation between latitude and **noon Sun angle** is

> For each degree of latitude that the place is away from the latitude where the noon Sun is overhead, the angle of the noon Sun becomes one degree *lower* from being vertical (or 90°) above the horizon (Figure 6).

37. Complete Table 2 by calculating the noon Sun angle for each of the indicated latitudes on the

Table 2 Noon Sun Angle Calculations

LATITUDE OF OVERHEAD NOON SUN	MAR 21 (___)	APR 11 (___)	JUN 21 (___)	DEC 22 (___)
	Noon Sun Angle			
90°N	____	____	____	____
40°N	50°	____	____	26½°
0°	____	____	66½°	____
20°S	____	62°	____	____

dates given. Some of the calculations have already been done.

38. From Table 2, the highest average noon Sun angle occurs at (40°N, 0°, 20°S). Circle your answer.

39. Calculate the noon Sun angle for your latitude on today's date.

    Date: _____

    Latitude of overhead noon Sun: _____

    Your latitude: _____

    Your noon Sun angle: _____

    (*Note:* You may want to compare your calculated noon Sun angle with a measured noon Sun angle obtained by using the technique described in the exercise "Astronomical Observations.")

40. Calculate the maximum and minimum noon Sun angles for your latitude.

MAXIMUM NOON SUN ANGLE	MINIMUM NOON SUN ANGLE
Date: _____	Date: _____
Angle: _____°	Angle: _____°

41. Calculate the average noon Sun angle (maximum plus minimum, divided by 2) and the range of the noon Sun angle (maximum minus minimum) for your location.

    Average noon Sun angle = _____°

    Range of the noon Sun angle = _____°

42. Describe some situations in which knowing the noon Sun angle might be useful.

    _____

    _____

Using Noon Sun Angle

One very practical use of noon Sun angle is in navigation. Like a navigator, you can determine your latitude if the date and angle of the noon Sun at your location are known. As you answer questions 43 and 44, keep in mind the relation between latitude and noon Sun angle (Figure 6).

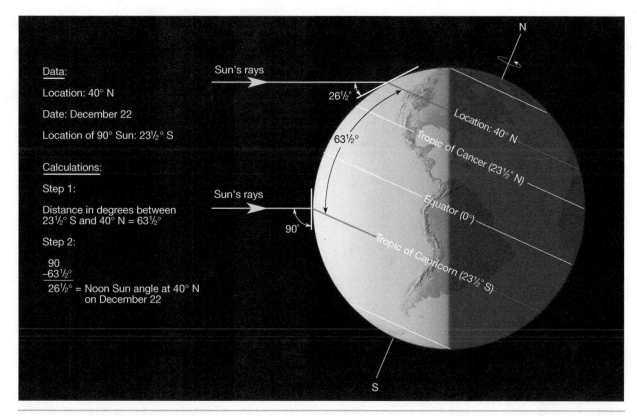

Figure 6 Calculating the noon Sun angle. Recall that on any given day, only one latitude receives vertical (90°) rays of the Sun. A place located 1° away (either north or south) receives an 89° angle at any location; a place 2° away, an 88° angle, and so forth. To calculate the noon Sun angle, simply find the number of degrees of latitude separating that location from the latitude that is receiving the vertical rays of the Sun. Then subtract that value from 90°. The example in this figure illustrates how to calculate the noon Sun angle for a city located at 40° north latitude on December 22 (winter solstice).

43. What is your latitude if, on March 21, you observe the noon Sun to the north at 18° above the horizon?

    Latitude: _____

44. What is your latitude if, on October 16, you observe the noon Sun to the south at 39° above the horizon?

    Latitude: _____

Solar Radiation at the Outer Edge of the Atmosphere

Table 3 shows the average daily radiation received at the outer edge of the atmosphere at select latitudes for different months.

To help visualize the pattern, plot the data from Table 3 on the graph in Figure 7. Using a different color for each latitude, draw lines through the monthly values to obtain yearly curves. Then answer questions 45–48.

45. Why do two periods of maximum solar radiation occur at the equator?

    _____

46. In June, why does the outer edge of the atmosphere at the equator receive less solar radiation than both the North Pole and 40°N latitude?

    _____

    _____

47. Why does the outer edge of the atmosphere at the North Pole receive no solar radiation in December?

    _____

48. What would be the approximate monthly values for solar radiation at the outer edge of the atmosphere at 40°S latitude? Explain how you arrived at the values.

    March: _____

    June: _____

    September: _____

    December: _____

    Explanation: _____

    _____

Table 3   Solar Radiation at the Outer Edge of the Atmosphere (langleys/day) at Various Latitudes during Select Months

LATITUDE	MARCH	JUNE	SEPTEMBER	DECEMBER
90°N	50	1050	50	0
40°N	700	950	720	325
0°	890	780	880	840

Earth–Sun Relations on the Internet

Apply the concepts from this exercise to an examination of solar and terrestrial radiation by completing the corresponding online activity on the *Applications & Investigations in Earth Science* website at http://prenhall.com/earthsciencelab

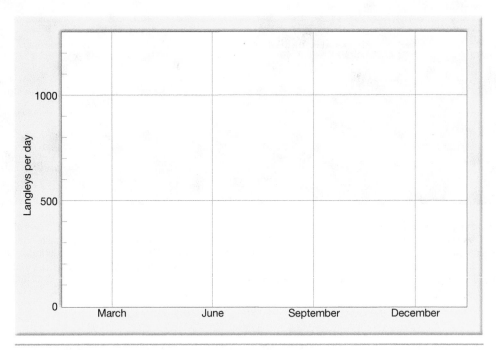

Figure 7   Graph of solar radiation received at the outer edge of the atmosphere.

Earth–Sun Relations

Date Due: _____

Name: _____

Date: _____

Class: _____

After you have finished this exercise, complete the following questions. You may have to refer to the exercise for assistance or to locate specific answers. Be prepared to submit this summary/report to your instructor at the designated time.

1. From Figure 3, what was the calculated percentage of solar radiation that is intercepted by each of the following 30° segments of latitude?

   0°–30° _____ %

   30°–60° _____ %

   60°–90° _____ %

2. How many hours of daylight occur at the following locations on the specified dates?

	MARCH 22	DECEMBER 22
40°N	_____ hrs	_____ hrs
0°	_____ hrs	_____ hrs
90°S	_____ hrs	_____ hrs

3. What is the noon Sun angle at these latitudes on April 11?

   40°N _____ °   0° _____ °

4. What is the relation between the angle of the noon Sun and the quantity of solar radiation received per square centimeter at the outer edge of the atmosphere?

   _____

   _____

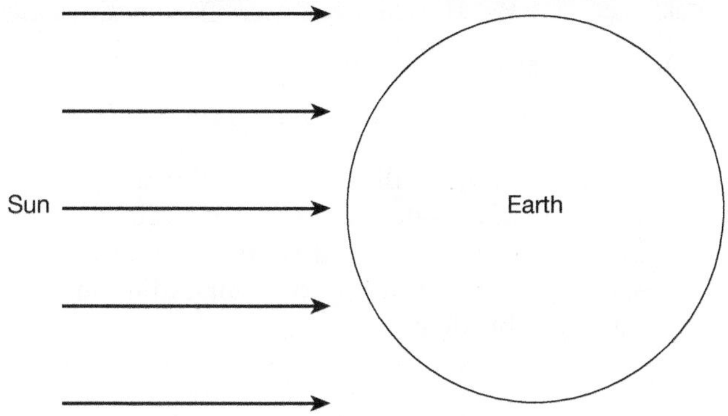

Figure 8 Earth's relation to the Sun on June 22.

5. Complete Figure 8 showing Earth's relation to the Sun on June 22. On the Earth, accurately draw and label the following:

   Axis
   Equator
   Tropic of Cancer
   Tropic of Capricorn
   Antarctic Circle
   Arctic Circle
   Circle of illumination
   Location of the overhead noon Sun

6. What causes the intensity and duration of solar radiation received at any place to vary throughout the year?

   _____

   _____

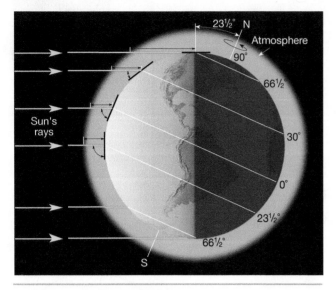

Figure 9 Earth–Sun relation diagram.

7. What is the date illustrated by the diagram in Figure 9? Calculate the noon Sun angle at 30° N latitude on this date and write a paragraph describing the distribution of solar radiation over Earth on this date.

_____

_____

_____

_____

8. What are the maximum and minimum noon Sun angles at your latitude?

Maximum noon Sun angle = _____° on _____ (date)

Minimum noon Sun angle = _____° on _____ (date)

9. What are the maximum and minimum durations of daylight at your latitude?

Maximum duration of daylight = _____ hrs

Minimum duration of daylight = _____ hrs

10. Write a brief statement describing how the intensity and duration of solar radiation change at your location throughout the year.

_____

_____

_____

_____

_____

11. The day is March 22. You view the noon Sun to the south at 35° above the horizon. What is your latitude?

Latitude: _____

146

Astronomical Observations

Scientific inquiry often starts with the systematic collection of data from which hypotheses and general theories are developed. The study of astronomy, an observational science, begins by carefully observing and recording the changing positions of the Sun, Moon, planets, and stars. To become proficient in astronomy requires developing the skills necessary to become a keen observer, using both the unaided eye and the telescope.

In this exercise you will observe several celestial objects. Observing and recording the changing positions of the Sun, Moon, and stars will aid in the interpretation and understanding of their movements in future exercises.

Objectives

After you have completed this exercise, you will have:

1. Records of the changing position of the Sun as it rises or sets on the horizon.
2. Measurements of the angle of the Sun above the horizon at noon on several days.
3. A record of the phases of the Moon over a period of several weeks.
4. Data on the times that the Moon rises and sets.
5. Records of the position and motion of stars.
6. An understanding of the parts of a telescope.

Materials

meterstick (or yardstick)	star chart	small weight
ruler	protractor	
calculator	stringatlas	

Materials Supplied by Your Instructor

telescope(s)   (optional)

Terms

revolution	altitude
astrolabe	rotation

Sun Observations

Many people are unaware that the Sun rises and sets at different locations on the horizon each day. As Earth **revolves** about the Sun, the orientation of its axis to the Sun continually changes. The result is that the location of the rising and setting Sun, as well as the **altitude** (angle above the horizon) of the Sun at noon, changes throughout the year.

Sunset (or Sunrise) Observations

Use the procedure presented in question 1 to make several observations and recordings of the Sun's location on the horizon at sunset or sunrise.

1. Following Steps 1–4, record at least four separate observations of the setting or rising Sun. Gather the data over a period of several weeks; *wait four or five days between each observation*. The directions are for sunset, although some minor adjustments will also allow their use for sunrise.

Step 1: Several minutes prior to sunset, estimate where the Sun will set on the western horizon. Draw the prominent features (buildings, trees, etc.) to the north and south of the Sun's approximate setting position on a sunset data sheet in Figure 1. (*Note:* As you observe the Sun setting in the west, south will be to your left and north to your right.)

CAUTION: Never look directly at the Sun; eye damage may result.

Step 2: As the Sun sets, draw its position on the data sheet relative to the fixed features on the horizon.

SUNSET (Sunrise) DATA SHEETS

HORIZON

Date of observation _____ Time of observation _____

HORIZON

Date of observation _____ Time of observation _____

HORIZON

Date of observation _____ Time of observation _____

HORIZON

Date of observation _____ Time of observation _____

Figure 1 Sunset (sunrise) data sheets.

Step 3: Note the date and time of your observation on the data sheet.

Step 4: Return to the same location several days later. Repeat your observation and record the results on a new data sheet.

2. After you complete your observations, describe the changing location of the Sun at sunset, or sunrise, that you have observed over the past several weeks.

_____

_____

_____

_____

Measuring the Noon Sun Angle

Observe the method for measuring the altitude (angle) of the noon Sun above the horizon illustrated in Figure 2. Then, following the steps listed in question 3, determine the altitude of the Sun at noon on several days.

3. To determine the altitude (angle) of the Sun at noon:

Step 1: Place a yardstick (a meterstick or ruler will do) perfectly vertical to the ground or a table top.

Step 2: When the Sun is at its highest position in the sky (noon, standard time, or 1 P.M. daylight savings time, will be close enough), accurately measure the length of the shadow.

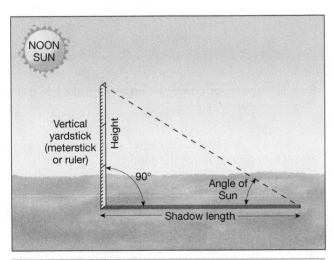

Figure 2 Illustration of the method for measuring the angle of the Sun above the horizon at noon. With each observation, be certain that the yardstick is perpendicular (at a 90° angle) to the ground or table top.

CAUTION: Never look directly at the Sun; eye damage may result.

Step 3: Divide the height of the stick by the length of the shadow.

Step 4: Consult Table 1 to determine the Sun angle. To find the Sun angle, locate the number on the table that comes closest to your answer from Step 3, and read the angle listed next to it.

Step 5: Repeat the measurement at exactly the same time on several different days over a period of four or five weeks. Record the dates and results of the measurements in the following spaces.

Date: _____   Noon Sun angle: _____°

Date: _____   Noon Sun angle: _____°

Date: _____   Noon Sun angle: _____°

Date: _____   Noon Sun angle: _____°

Answer questions 4–6 after you have completed your measurements of the altitude of the noon Sun.

4. The altitude of the noon Sun has (increased, decreased) over the period of the measurements. Circle your answer.

5. How many degrees has the noon Sun angle changed over the period of your observations?

_____°

6. What is the approximate average change of the noon Sun angle per day?

_____° per day

7. Based on your answer in question 6, how many degrees will the noon Sun angle change over a six-month period?

_____° over a six-month period

Moon Observations

Most people have noticed that the shape of the illuminated portion of the Moon as observed from Earth changes regularly. However, few take the time to systematically record and explain these changes. Following the procedure presented in question 8, begin your study of the Moon by observing its phases and recording your observations.

8. Record at least four observations of the Moon by completing each of the following steps regularly at a two- or three-day interval.

Step 1: On a Moon observation data sheet provided in Figure 3, indicate the approximate east–west

Table 1 Data Table for Determining the Noon Sun Angle. Select the nearest number to the quotient determined by dividing the height of the stick by the length of the shadow. Read the corresponding Sun angle.

IF HEIGHT OF STICK / LENGTH OF SHADOW	THEN SUN ANGLE IS	IF HEIGHT OF STICK / LENGTH OF SHADOW	THEN SUN ANGLE IS
0.2679	15°	1.235	51°
0.2867	16°	1.280	52°
0.3057	17°	1.327	53°
0.3249	18°	1.376	54°
0.3443	19°	1.428	55°
0.3640	20°	1.483	56°
0.3839	21°	1.540	57°
0.4040	22°	1.600	58°
0.4245	23°	1.664	59°
0.4452	24°	1.732	60°
0.4663	25°	1.804	61°
0.4877	26°	1.881	62°
0.5095	27°	1.963	63°
0.5317	28°	2.050	64°
0.5543	29°	2.145	65°
0.5774	30°	2.246	66°
0.6009	31°	2.356	67°
0.6249	32°	2.475	68°
0.6494	33°	2.605	69°
0.6745	34°	2.748	70°
0.7002	35°	2.904	71°
0.7265	36°	3.078	72°
0.7536	37°	3.271	73°
0.7813	38°	3.487	74°
0.8098	39°	3.732	75°
0.8391	40°	4.011	76°
0.8693	41°	4.332	77°
0.9004	42°	4.705	78°
0.9325	43°	5.145	79°
0.9657	44°	5.671	80°
1.0000	45°	6.314	81°
1.0360	46°	7.115	82°
1.0720	47°	8.144	83°
1.1110	48°	9.514	84°
1.1500	49°	11.430	85°
1.1920	50°		

position of the Moon in the sky by drawing a circle at the appropriate location. (*Note:* As you look to the south to observe the Moon, east will be to your left and west to your right.)

Step 2: By shading the circle, indicate the shape of the illuminated portion of the Moon you observe.

Step 3: Note the date and time of your observation on the data sheet.

Step 4: Keep in mind that the approximate time between moonrise on the eastern horizon and moonset on the western horizon is twelve hours. Estimate when the Moon may have risen and when it may set. Write your estimates on the data sheet.

Step 5: Repeat your observation in several days, using a new data sheet.

Answer questions 9–12 after you have completed all your observations of the Moon.

9. What happened to the size and shape of the illuminated portion of the Moon over the period of your observations?

MOON OBSERVATION DATA SHEETS

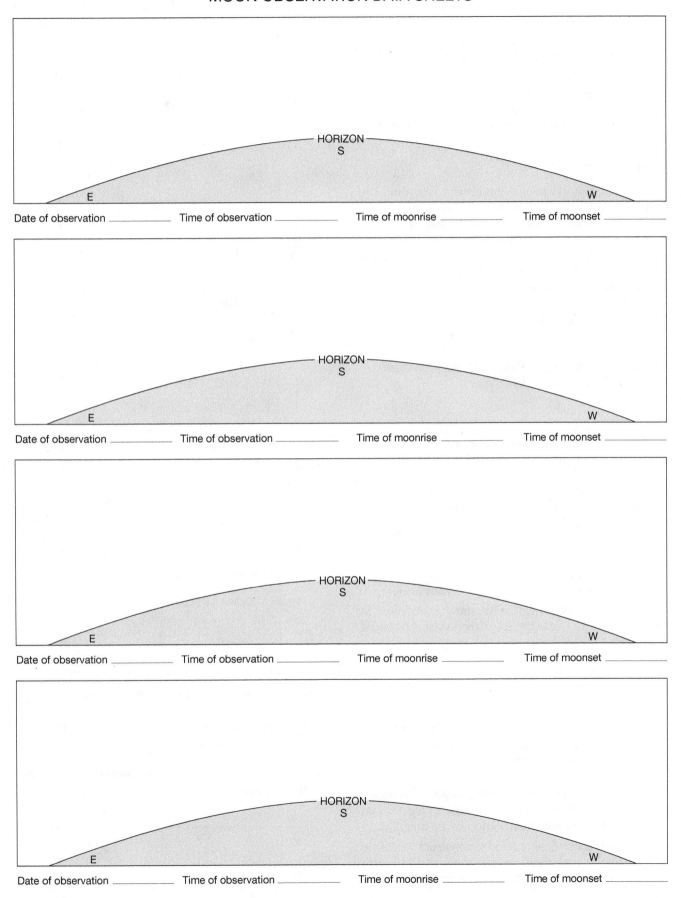

Figure 3   Moon observation data sheets.

10. The Moon moved farther (eastward, westward) in the sky with each successive observation. Circle your answer.

11. The times of moonrise and moonset became (earlier, later) with each successive observation. Circle your answer.

12. Based upon your observations and your answers to questions 10 and 11, the Moon revolves around Earth from (east to west, west to east).

Star Observations

Throughout history, people have been recording the positions and nightly movement of stars that result from Earth's **rotation**, as well as the seasonal changes in the constellations as Earth revolves about the Sun. Early astronomers offered many explanations for the changes before the true nature of the motions was understood in the 17th century.

To best observe the stars, select a suitable dark area on a clear, moonless night. Then complete questions 13–22.

13. Make a list of the different colors of the stars you can observe in the sky.

_____

Select one star that is overhead, or nearly so, and observe its movement over a period of one hour.

14. With your arm extended, approximately how many widths of your fist has the position of the star changed?

_____ fist widths

15. The star appears to move (eastward, westward) over a period of one hour. Circle your answer.

16. How is the movement of the star you observed in question 15 related to the direction of rotation of Earth?

_____

_____

Use a suitable star chart to locate several constellations and the North Star (Polaris).

17. Refer to Figure 4. Sketch the pattern of stars for two constellations you were able to locate. List the name of each constellation by its diagram.

18. Using Figure 5 as a guide, construct a simple **astrolabe** and measure the angle of the North Star (Polaris) above the horizon as accurately as

Constellation Star Pattern

Constellation name: _____

Constellation Star Pattern

Constellation name: _____

Figure 4 Constellation sketches.

possible.

_____° above the (north, south) horizon

Over a period of several hours, observe the motion of the stars in the vicinity of Polaris.

19. Write a brief summary of the motion of the stars in the vicinity of Polaris.

_____

_____

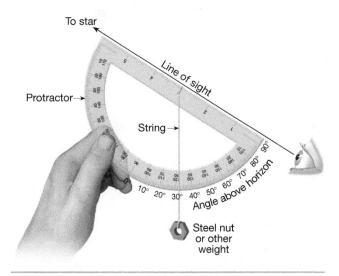

To star

Protractor→

Line of sight

String →

10° 20° 30° 40° 50° 60° 70° 80° 90°

Angle above horizon

Steel nut
or other
weight

Figure 5 Simple astrolabe, an instrument used to measure the angle of an object above the horizon. The angle is read where the string crosses the outer edge of the protractor, 32° in the example illustrated. Notice that the angle above the horizon is the difference between 90° and the angle imprinted on the protractor.

If you can, come back to the same location at the exact same time, several weeks later.

20. The same star you observed overhead several weeks earlier (is still overhead, has moved to the east, has moved to the west). Circle your answer.

21. How is the change in position of the star you observed overhead several weeks earlier related to the revolution of Earth?

_____

_____

_____

22. Using the astrolabe you constructed in question 18, repeat your measurement of the angle of the North Star (Polaris) above the horizon. List your new measurement and compare it to the measurement you obtained several weeks earlier. Explain your result(s).

_____

_____

_____

Astronomical Observations on the Internet

Continue your analyses of the topics presented in this exercise by completing the corresponding online activity on the *Applications & Investigations in Earth Science* website at http://prenhall.com/earthsciencelab

Notes and calculations.

Astronomical Observations

Date Due: _____

Name: _____

Date: _____

Class: _____

After you have finished this exercise, complete the following questions. You may have to refer to the exercise for assistance or to locate specific answers. Be prepared to submit this summary/report to your instructor at the designated time.

1. On Figure 6, prepare a single sketch illustrating your observed positions of the setting (or rising) Sun on the horizon during the past several weeks. Show the reference features you used on the horizon. Label each position of the Sun with the date of the observation. Write a brief summary of your observations below the diagram.

2. From question 3, step 5, in the exercise, list the noon Sun angle that you calculated for the first and last day of your measurements.

   Noon Sun angle on the first day: _____ °

   Date of observation: _____

   Noon Sun angle on the last day: _____ °

   Date of observation: _____

3. Draw two sketches of the Moon—the first illustrating the Moon as you saw it on your first lunar observation, the second as you saw it on your last observation. Label the date and time of each observation.

FIRST MOON OBSERVATION	LAST MOON OBSERVATION
Date: _____	Date: _____
Time: _____	Time: _____

4. Did the Moon rise earlier or later each night that you observed it?

_____

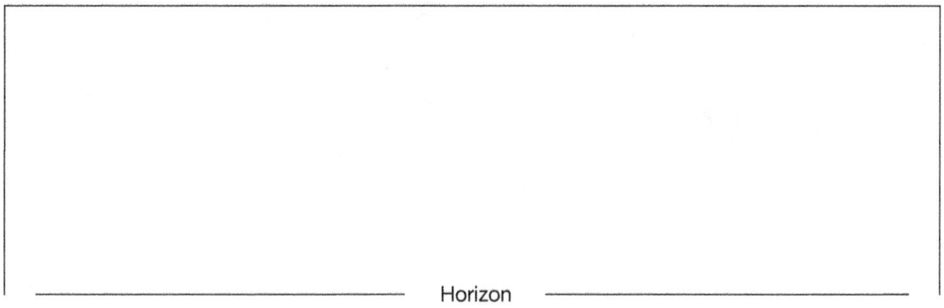

Horizon

Summary: _____

_____

_____

Figure 6 Sunset (sunrise) observations.

5. List the different colors of stars that you observed.

_____

6. Approximately how many widths of your fist, with your arm extended, will a star appear to move in one hour? Toward which direction do the stars appear to move throughout the night and what is the reason for the motion?

_____

_____

_____

7. What was your measured angle of the North Star (Polaris) above the horizon at your location? Did the angle change over a several-week period? Explain why.

_____

_____

_____

8. Refer to Figure 7. Sketch the pattern of stars for any constellation you have been able to locate in the sky. What is the name of the constellation?

Constellation Star Pattern

Constellation name: _____

Figure 7 Constellation sketch.

Patterns in the Solar System

Although composed of many diverse objects, the solar system (Figure 1) exhibits various degrees of order and several regular patterns. To simplify the investigation of planetary sizes, masses, etc., the planets can be arranged into two distinct groups, with the members of each displaying similar attributes. This exercise examines the physical properties and motions of the planets with the goal of summarizing these characteristics in a few general, easily remembered statements.

Objectives

After you have completed this exercise, you should be able to:

1. Describe the appearance of the solar system when it is viewed along the plane of the ecliptic.
2. Summarize the distances and spacing of the planets in the solar system.

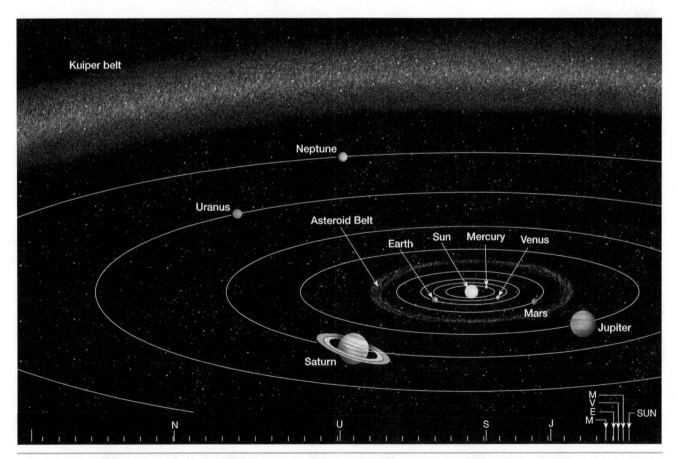

Figure 1 The solar system showing the orbits of the planets to scale. A different scale has been used for the sizes of the Sun and planets. Therefore, the diagram is not a true scale model representation of the solar system.

3. Summarize and compare the physical characteristics of the terrestrial and Jovian planets.
4. Describe the motions of the planets in the solar system.

Materials

ruler
colored pencils
calculator

Materials Supplied by Your Instructor

4-meter length of adding machine paper
meterstick
light source (150-watt bulb)
black containers with covers and thermometers

Terms

nebula
terrestrial planets
Jovian planets
dwarf planets
plane of the ecliptic
mass
density
weight
rotation
revolution
Kepler's laws
astronomical unit

Introduction

The order that exists within the solar system is directly related to the laws of physics that governed its formation. Astronomers have determined that the Sun and planets originated approximately 4.6 billion years ago from an enormous cloud of dust and gas. As this **nebula** contracted, it began to rotate and flatten. Eventually the temperature and pressure in the center of the cloud was great enough to initiate nuclear fusion and form the Sun.

Near the center of the nebula, the planets Mercury, Venus, Earth, and Mars evolved under nearly the same conditions and consequently exhibit similar physical properties. Because these planets are rocky objects with solid surfaces, they are collectively called the **terrestrial (Earth-like) planets**.

The outer planets, Jupiter, Saturn, Uranus, and Neptune, being farther from the Sun than the terrestrial planets, formed under much colder conditions and are gaseous objects with central cores of ices and rock. Since the four planets are very similar, they are often grouped together and called the **Jovian (Jupiterlike) planets**.

The **dwarf planets**, which include, among other celestial objects, Pluto and the former asteroid Ceres, are not included with either the terrestrial or Jovian planets.

Table 1 illustrates many of the individual characteristics of the planets in the solar system.

1. Examine the data in Table 1, then
   a. Draw lines on the upper and lower parts of Table 1 that separate the terrestrial planets from the Jovian planets. Label the lines "Belt of Asteroids."

Table 1 Planetary data.

		Mean Distance from Sun					Orbital Velocity	
Planet	Symbol	AU	Millions of Miles	Millions of Kilometers	Period of Revolution	Inclination of Orbit	mi/s	km/s
Mercury	☿	0.387	36	58	88^{d}	7°00′	29.5	47.5
Venus	♀	0.723	67	108	224.7^{d}	3°24′	21.8	35.0
Earth	⊕	1.000	93	150	365.25^{d}	0°00′	18.5	29.8
Mars	♂	1.524	142	228	687^{d}	1°51′	14.9	24.1
Jupiter	♃	5.203	483	778	11.86^{yr}	1°18′	8.1	13.1
Saturn	♄	9.539	886	1427	29.46^{yr}	2°29′	6.0	9.6
Uranus	⛢	19.180	1783	2870	84^{yr}	0°46′	4.2	6.8
Neptune	♆	30.060	2794	4497	165^{yr}	1°46′	3.3	5.3

		Diameter						
Planet	Period of Rotation	Miles	Kilometers	Relative Mass (Earth = 1)	Average Density (g/cm^3)	Polar Flattening (%)	Mean Temperature (°C)	Number of Known Satellites
Mercury	59^{d}	3015	4854	0.056	5.4	0.0	167	0
Venus	244^{d}	7526	12,112	0.82	5.2	0.0	464	0
Earth	$23^{h}56^{m}04^{s}$	7920	12,751	1.00	5.5	0.3	15	1
Mars	$24^{h}37^{m}23^{s}$	4216	6788	0.108	3.9	0.5	−65	2
Jupiter	$9^{h}50^{m}$	88,700	143,000	317.87	1.3	6.7	−110	63
Saturn	$10^{h}14^{m}$	75,000	121,000	95.14	0.7	10.4	−140	56
Uranus	$17^{h}14^{m}$	29,000	47,000	14.56	1.2	2.3	−195	27
Neptune	$16^{h}03^{m}$	28,900	46,529	17.21	1.7	1.8	−200	13

b. On both parts of the table write the word "terrestrial" next to Mercury, Venus, Earth, and Mars and the word "Jovian" next to Jupiter, Saturn, Uranus, and Neptune.

The "Shape" of the Solar System

When the solar system is viewed from the side, the orbits of the planets all lie in nearly the same plane, called the **plane of the ecliptic** (Figure 1). The column labeled "Inclination of Orbit" in Table 1 lists how many degrees the orbit of each planet is inclined from the plane. Answer questions 2–4 by referring to Table 1.

2. Other than Mercury, whose orbit is inclined (4, 7, 10) degrees, the orbits of the remaining planets are all within (4, 7, 10) degrees of the plane of the ecliptic. Circle your answers.

3. The orbit of the dwarf planet Pluto is inclined 17° to the plane. When compared to the eight planets, Pluto's orbit is:

_____

4. Considering the nebular origin of the solar system, suggest a reason why the orbits of the planets are nearly all in the same plane.

_____

_____

Distance and Spacing of the Planets

An examination of any scale-model solar system reveals that the distances from the Sun and the spacing between the planets appear to follow a regular pattern. Although many ancient astronomers were concerned with planetary distances and spacing, it was not until the mid-1700s that astronomers found a simple mathematical relation that described the arrangement of the planets known at the time.

A Scale Model of Planetary Distances

Perhaps the best way to examine distance and spacing of the planets in the solar system is to use a scale model.

5. Prepare a distance scale model of the solar system according to the following steps.

Step 1: Obtain a 4-meter length of adding machine paper and a meterstick from your instructor.

Step 2: Draw an "X" about 10 centimeters from one end of the adding machine paper and label it "Sun."

Step 3: Using the mean distances of the planets from the Sun in miles presented in Table 1 and the following scale, draw a small circle for each planet at its proper scale mile distance from the Sun. Use a different colored pencil for the terrestrial and Jovian planets and write the name of the planet next to its position.

SCALE

1 millimeter = 1 million miles

1 centimeter = 10 million miles

1 meter = 1,000 million miles

Step 4: Write the word "asteroids" 258 million scale miles from the Sun.

Answer questions 6–9 using the distance scale model you constructed in question 5.

6. What feature of the solar system separates the terrestrial planets from the Jovian planets?

_____

7. Observe the scale model diagram and summarize the spacing for each of the two groups of planets.

Spacing of the terrestrial planets: _____

_____

Spacing of the Jovian planets: _____

_____

8. Write a brief statement that describes the spacing of the planets in the solar system.

_____

_____

9. Which planet(s) vary the most from the general pattern of spacing?

_____

Comparing the Terrestrial and Jovian Planets

The physical characteristics such as diameter, density, and mass of the terrestrial planets are very similar and can be summarized in a few statements. Likewise, the characteristics exhibited by the Jovian planets as a group can also be generalized.

To gain an understanding of the similarities of the planets within each of the two groups and the contrasts between the two groups, complete the following sections using the planetary data presented in Table 1.

Size of the Planets

The similarities in the diameters of the planets within each of the two groups and the contrast between the groups are perhaps the most obvious patterns in the solar system. The diameter of each planet is given in both miles and kilometers in Table 1.

10. To visually compare the relative sizes of the planets and Sun, complete the following steps using the unmarked side of your 4-meter length of adding machine paper.

Step 1: Determine the radius of each planet in kilometers by dividing its diameter (in kilometers) by 2. List your answers in the "Radius" column of Table 2.

Step 2: Use a scale of 1 cm = 2,000 km. Determine the scale model radius of each planet and list your answer in the "Scale Model Radius" column of Table 2.

Step 3: Draw an "X" about 10 cm from one end of the adding machine paper and label it "Starting point."

Step 4: Using the scale model radius in Table 2, begin at the starting point and mark the radius of each planet with a line on the paper. Use a different colored pencil for the terrestrial and Jovian planets. Label each line with the planet's name.

Step 5: The diameter of the Sun is approximately 1,350,000 kilometers. Using the same scale as you used for the planets (1 cm = 2000 km), determine the scale model radius of the Sun. Mark the Sun's radius on the adding machine paper using a different colored pencil from the two planet groups. Label the line "Sun."

Answer questions 11–17 using both Table 1 and the scale model radius diagram you constructed in question 10.

11. Which is the largest of the terrestrial planets and what is its diameter?

_____, _____ miles

12. Which is the smallest Jovian planet and what is its diameter?

_____, _____ miles

13. Complete the following statement.

The smallest Jovian planet, _____, is _____ times larger than the largest terrestrial planet.

14. Summarize the sizes of the planets within each group.

The diameters of the terrestrial planets: _____

_____

The diameters of the Jovian planets: _____

_____

15. Write a general statement that compares the sizes of the terrestrial planets to those of the Jovian planets.

_____

_____

16. Complete the following statement.

The Sun is _____ times larger than Earth and _____ times larger than Jupiter.

17. The diameter of the dwarf planet Pluto is approximately 1,500 miles, which is about (one-third, one-half, twice) the diameter of the smallest planet. Circle your answer.

Table 2 Planetary Radii with Scale Model Equivalents

Planet	Radius (in kilometers)	Scale Model Radius
Mercury	_____	_____ cm
Venus	_____	_____ cm
Earth	_____	_____ cm
Mars	_____	_____ cm
Jupiter	_____	_____ cm
Saturn	_____	_____ cm
Uranus	_____	_____ cm
Neptune	_____	_____ cm

Mass and Density of the Planets

Mass is a measure of the quantity of matter an object contains. In Table 1 the masses of the planets are given in relation to the mass of Earth. For example, the mass of Mercury is given as 0.056, which means that it consists of only a small fraction of the quantity of matter that Earth contains. On the other hand, the Jovian planets all contain several times more matter than Earth.

Density is the mass per unit volume of a substance. In Table 1 the average densities of the planets are expressed in grams per cubic centimeter (g/cm^3). As a reference, the density of water is approximately one gram per cubic centimeter.

Using the relative masses of the planets given in Table 1, answer questions 18–22.

18. Complete the following statements:

a. The planet _____ is the most massive planet in the solar system. It is _____ times more massive than Earth.

b. The least massive planet is _____, which contains only _____ as much mass as Earth.

The gravitational attraction of a planet is directly related to its mass.

19. Which planet exerts the greatest, and which the least, pull of gravity? Explain your answer.

_____

_____

Your **weight** is a function of the gravitational attraction of an object on your mass.

20. The surface gravities of Mars and Jupiter are respectively about 0.4 and 2.5 that of Earth. What would be your approximate weight on each of these planets?

_____

21. Which of the two groups of planets would have the greatest ability to hold large quantities of gas as part of their compositions? Explain your answer.

_____

_____

22. Write a general statement comparing the masses and gravitational attractions of the terrestrial planets to those of the Jovian planets.

_____

_____

Diameter versus Density

To visually compare the diameters and densities of the planets, use the data in Table 1 to complete the diameter versus density graph, Figure 2, according to the procedure in question 23.

23. Plot a point on the diameter verses density graph, Figure 2, for each planet where its diameter intersects its density. Label each point with the planet's name. Use a different colored pencil for the terrestrial and Jovian planets.

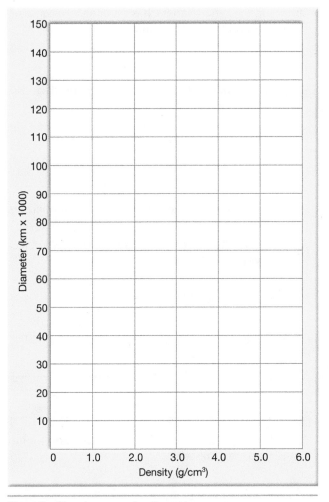

Figure 2 Diameter verses density graph.

Answer questions 24–34 using Table 1 and the diameter verses density graph you constructed in question 23.

24. What general relation exists between a planet's size and its density?

_____

25. Consider the fact that the densities of the two rocks that form the majority of Earth's surface, the igneous rocks granite and basalt, are each about 3.0 g/cm³. Therefore, the average density of the terrestrial planets is (greater, less than) the density of Earth's surface. Circle your answer.

26. The term (rocky, gaseous) best describes the terrestrial planets. Circle your answer.

27. The average density of Earth is about 5.5 g/cm³. Considering that the densities of the surface rocks are much less than the average, what does this suggest about the density of Earth's interior?

_____

161

28. Which of the planets has a density less than water and therefore would "float"?

_____

29. Write a brief statement comparing the densities of the Jovian planets to the density of water.

_____

_____

30. The Jovian planets can be best described as (rocky, ice, and gas) worlds. Circle your answer.

31. Explain why Jupiter can be such a massive object and yet have such a low density.

_____

32. Write a general statement comparing the densities of the terrestrial planets to the Jovian planets.

_____

_____

33. Why are the densities of the terrestrial and Jovian planets so different?

_____

_____

34. The mass of Pluto, about 0.002 that of Earth's, is most like the masses of the (terrestrial, Jovian) planets, while its density of approximately 2.0 gm/cm^3 is similar to the (terrestrial, Jovian) planets. This suggests that this dwarf planet is made of (solid rock, a rock and ice mixture, all gas). Circle the correct responses.

Number of Moons of the Planets

The column labeled "Number of Known Satellites" in Table 1 indicates the number of known moons orbiting each planet.

35. Write a brief statement comparing the number of known moons of the terrestrial planets to the number orbiting the Jovian planets.

_____

_____

36. What is the general relation between the number of moons a planet has compared to its mass? Suggest a reason for the relation.

_____

_____

_____

Rotation and Revolution of the Planets

Rotation is the turning of a planet about its axis that is responsible for day and night. When the solar system is viewed from above the Northern Hemisphere of Earth, the planets, with the exception of Venus, rotate in a counterclockwise direction. Venus exhibits a very slow clockwise rotation. The time that it takes for a planet to complete one 360° rotation on its axis is called the _period of rotation_. The units used to measure a planet's period of rotation are Earth hours and days.

Revolution is the motion of a planet around the Sun. The time that it takes a planet to complete one revolution about the Sun is the length of its year, called the _period of revolution_. The units used to measure a planet's period of revolution are Earth days and years. Without exception, the direction of revolution of the planets is counterclockwise around the Sun when the solar system is viewed from above the Northern Hemisphere of Earth.

Use the planetary data in Table 1 to answer questions 37–46.

37. If you could live on Venus or Jupiter, approximately how long would you have to wait between sunrises?

On Venus a sunrise would occur every _____ days.

On Jupiter a sunrise would occur every _____ hours.

38. Write a statement comparing the periods of rotation of the terrestrial planets to those of the Jovian planets.

_____

_____

The giant planet Jupiter rotates once on its axis approximately every 10 hours. If an object were on the equator of the planet and rotating with it, it would travel approximately 280,000 miles (the equatorial circumference or distance around the equator) in about 10 hours.

39. Calculate the equatorial rotational velocity of Jupiter using the following formula.

$$\text{Velocity} = \frac{\text{Distance}}{\text{Time}} = \frac{\underline{\hspace{2cm}} \text{ mi}}{\underline{\hspace{2cm}} \text{ hr}}$$

$$= \underline{\hspace{3cm}} \text{mi/hr}$$

40. The equatorial circumference of Earth is about 24,000 miles. What is the approximate equatorial rotational velocity of Earth?

_____ miles/hour

41. How many times faster is Jupiter's equatorial rotational velocity than Earth's?

_____ times faster

42. Compare the planets' periods of rotation to their periods of revolution and then complete the following statement by circling the correct responses.

The terrestrial planets all have (long, short) days and (long, short) years, while the Jovian planets all have (long, short) days and (short, long) years.

43. In one Earth year, how many revolutions will the planet Mercury complete and what fraction of a revolution will Neptune accomplish?

Mercury: _____ revolutions in one Earth year

Neptune: _____ of a revolution in one Earth year

44. On Venus, how many days (sunrises) would there be in each of its years?

_____ day(s) per year

45. How many days (rotations) will Mercury complete in one of its years?

Mercury: _____ Mercury days in one Mercury year

46. Explain the relation between a planet's period of rotation and period of revolution that would cause one side of a planet to face the Sun throughout its year.

_____

_____

In the early 1600s Johannes Kepler set forth three laws of planetary motion. According to Kepler's third law, the period of revolution of a planet, measured in Earth years, is related to its distance from the Sun in astronomical units (one **astronomical unit (AU)** is defined as the average distance from the Sun to Earth—93 million miles or 150 million kilometers). The law states that a planet's orbital period squared is equal to its mean solar distance cubed ($p^2 = d^3$).

47. Applying Kepler's third law, what would be the period of revolution of a hypothetical planet that is 4 AUs from the Sun? Show your calculation in the following space.

_____

_____

_____

Terrestrial Planet Temperatures

The temperature of an object is related to the intensity of the heat source, its distance from the source, and the nature of the material it is composed of. To better understand how these variables influence the temperatures of the terrestrial planets, observe the equipment in the laboratory (Figure 3) and then complete the following steps. Answer questions 48–51 after you complete your investigation.

Step 1: Working in groups of four or more, obtain four *identical* light (heat) sources and four *identical* black containers with covers and thermometers.

Step 2: Conduct four experiments simultaneously, one by each member of the group. Do one experiment with the covered can and thermometer 15 cm from the light source, another with the can 30 cm from the light source, the third 45 cm, and the fourth 60 cm.

Step 3: Note the starting temperature for each container on Table 3; the temperatures should all be the same.

Step 4: For each of the four setups, turn on the light and record the temperature of the container exactly 10 minutes later. Record the temperatures in Table 3.

Step 5: Using the temperature scale on the left axis of the graph, plot the temperatures from Table 3

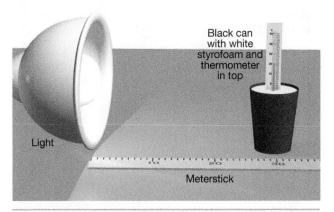

Black can with white styrofoam and thermometer in top

Light

Meterstick

Figure 3 Terrestrial planet temperatures lab-equipment setup.

Table 3 Temperature Data

Distance from Light Source (cm)	Starting Temperature (°C)	10-minute Temperature
15		
30		
45		
60		

on the graph in Figure 4. Connect the points and label the graph "temperature change with distance."

Step 6: In Table 1, notice the mean temperatures for the planets. Plot the mean temperatures of the terrestrial planets at their proper locations on the graph, Figure 4. Assume a scale of 40 cm equals 1 AU and use the temperature scale on the right axis of the graph. Label each point with the planet's name. Connect the points and label the graph "mean terrestrial planet temperatures."

48. The "temperature change with distance" graph represents how you would expect that, everything else being equal, the temperature of a planet would be related to its distance from the Sun.

In the following space, write a brief description of the "temperature change with distance" graph.

_____

_____

_____

49. The "mean terrestrial planet temperatures" graph represents the real mean temperatures of the planets. Compare this graph to the theoretical "temperature change with distance graph." How are the graphs similar? How are they different?

_____

_____

_____

_____

_____

50. Write a brief statement suggesting the reason(s) for the difference(s) between the two graphs you noted in question 49.

_____

_____

_____

_____

_____

51. Complete your investigation by writing a statement describing the mean temperatures of the terrestrial planets and the variables that determine those temperatures.

_____

_____

_____

_____

_____

The Solar System on the Internet

Continue your analyses of the topics presented in this exercise by completing the corresponding online activity on the *Applications & Investigations in Earth Science* website at http://prenhall.com/earthsciencelab

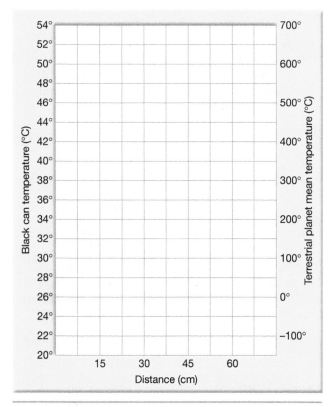

Figure 4 Terrestrial planet temperatures graph.

Patterns in the Solar System

Date Due: _____

Name: _____

Date: _____

Class: _____

After you have finished this exercise, complete the following questions. You may have to refer to the exercise for assistance or to locate specific answers. Be prepared to submit this summary/report to your instructor at the designated time.

1. On Figure 5, prepare a sketch illustrating the planets Mercury, Venus, Earth, and Mars at their approximate distance from the Sun. View the solar system from above the Northern Hemisphere of Earth. Draw arrows around each planet to illustrate its direction of rotation. Also, draw an arrow in the orbit of each planet that shows the direction of revolution.

2. Briefly describe the spacing of the planets in the solar system.

_____

_____

_____

3. Define the following terms:

Terrestrial planets: _____

_____

Jovian planets: _____

_____

Plane of the ecliptic: _____

_____

Rotation: _____

_____

Mass: _____

_____

Astronomical unit: _____

_____

Figure 5 Spacing and motion of the terrestrial planets.

4. Referring to the nebular origin of the solar system, describe and explain the direction of revolution of the planets.

_____

_____

_____

5. Write a brief statement for each of the following characteristics that compares the terrestrial to the Jovian planets.

Diameter: _____

_____

_____

Density: _____

_____

_____

Period of rotation: _____

_____

_____

Number of moons: _____

_____

_____

Mass: _____

_____

_____

6. If you knew the distance of a planet from the Sun, explain how you would calculate its period of revolution.

_____

_____

_____

7. How does a planet's distance from the Sun affect the solar radiation the planet receives? Why?

_____

_____

_____

8. How are the mean temperatures of the terrestrial planets related to the solar radiation they intercept? What is the explanation for any discrepancy?

_____

_____

_____

9. Considering what you have learned about general patterns in the solar system, after reexamining the characteristics of Pluto, discuss why this former planet was reclassified as a dwarf planet in 2006.

_____

_____

_____

Index